The Basic Process of
Food-making in Green Plants

Photosynthesis

Jerome L. Rosenberg

Holt, Rinehart and Winston, Inc., New York

Jerome L. Rosenberg is Professor of Chemistry at the University of Pittsburgh, where since 1953 he has conducted a research program in photosynthesis and in more general aspects of photochemistry.

Preface

The study of photosynthesis is one of the many areas of science in which research activity has accelerated since World War II. There are a number of reasons for this intensified effort, which has produced many new exciting experimental results and new interpretations of the fundamental basis of this important life process.

One reason is the improvement in experimental techniques that has marked the growth of science in recent years. Radioactive isotopes for tracer experiments have become readily available. Simple methods for separating and analyzing complex mixtures of chemical substances found in living cells have become routine laboratory procedures. Electron microscopy has been refined to a point where very large individual molecules can almost be resolved. Improvements in electronic and optical devices have produced a wide variety of light sources for the laboratory and precise instruments for measuring the diverse responses of matter to light.

Even more important than the improvements in technique have been the changes in attitudes toward science. More gifted students are selecting careers in the natural sciences, and an increasing number of educational institutions are developing strong scientific research programs. The major reason for advances in our understanding of photosynthesis, however, has been the broadening of the base of the scientific approach to this problem. Now not only biologists, but chemists and physicists as well are taking important roles in this work. Every biological process, no matter how complex, must obey the fundamental laws of physics and chemistry. Scientists schooled in all disciplines are needed to find the connections between the simple laws of nature and the seemingly complicated workings of the intact photosynthetic machinery of plants. Thus the more varied the technical backgrounds and points of view brought to this concerted study, the more unified and coherent are the different experimental observations.

This book was written to show beginning science students how progress has been made in applying concepts of physics and chemistry to the problem of photosynthesis. The scientific device of the model has been used, in which scientists construct in their minds a schematic model of how photosynthesis works. The scientific language of chemistry and physics has been left out almost completely, so that the reader who cannot interpret a chemical formula or a complicated algebraic equation will not be discouraged from trying to understand what is even more important, the logical flow of ideas characteristic of these sciences.

A consequence of the inter-disciplinary approach is that every scientist who chooses to study photosynthesis must learn something of the methodology of all the sciences. Nevertheless, the view that any one person has of the whole problem must of necessity be a partisan one, taken from the vantage point of his own scientific background. In particular, I make no claim of universality for my point of view. It is the outlook of a physical chemist who has been particularly interested in the regularities of photochemical behavior of large molecules. My first education in photosynthesis was an apprenticeship with two great scientists, Professors James Franck, physicist, and Hans Gaffron, biochemist, who proved by their own example that men of widely different backgrounds and points of reference can and must work together to uncode nature's secrets.

I am grateful to colleagues who have allowed the use of their illustrative material for this book, including Dr. J. A. Bassham of the Lawrence Radiation Laboratory of the University of California at Berkeley, Dr. John Bergeron of the Brookhaven National Laboratory, and Dr. J. J. Wolken of the University of Pittsburgh Medical School and Carnegie Institute of Technology.

Contents

1

The Role of Photosynthesis

The process by which plants make use of light from the sun to synthesize the complicated substances needed for life and growth has been a source of fascination to generations of scientists. From the smallest single-celled algae, measuring less than a hundredth of a millimeter in diameter, to the leaves of giant trees, all sizes and shapes of green plants perform photosynthesis according to a pattern that is remarkably uniform throughout the plant kingdom. The attempt to discover the common essential features of this process in a living world of such diversity has occupied scientists of many disciplines, including biologists, chemists, physicists, mathematicians, geologists, and even astronomers. The results of this attempt are the subject of this book.

The basic equation of photosynthesis—the production of sugar and oxygen from carbon dioxide and water—has been known for less than two hundred years. Photosynthesis is a chemical process, and the methods of chemistry are required for studying it. These methods were not developed until the last half of the eighteenth century. During that period, men like Karl Wilhelm Scheele, Joseph Priestley, and Antoine Lavoisier were laying the basis for the systematic description of chemical substances, of their interactions, and of their exact composition. Chemical observations were extended for the first time beyond the more familiar liquids and solids to include gases. Experiments were designed to confine and measure gases within a closed apparatus.

The discovery of one atmospheric gas, oxygen, was crucial in this revolutionary period of development in chemistry and biology. Although oxygen is an odorless, invisible gas, indirect methods were found for observing and analyzing it. One of the most important experiments was performed by the English scientist Joseph Priestley. Priestley discovered that a burning candle and a living mouse both extracted the same substance from the atmosphere. When a candle was burned in a closed jar, the flame eventually went out. If a mouse were then placed in the jar, it quickly died. Priestley observed by chance that a sprig of mint placed in water in such an atmosphere had the effect of restoring the "injured" air to its normal state. A mouse now placed in the jar thrived as though it were breathing atmospheric air. The unknown substance was, of course, oxygen. Actually Scheele, Priestley, and Lavoisier all discovered oxygen independently. Scheele, a Swedish chemist who also discovered nitrogen, was the first to isolate oxygen. But Priestley was the first to publish his results. Lavoisier, the great French chemist who is generally considered to be the founder of modern chemistry, gave oxygen its name.

The observation made by Priestley in 1774 was quickly followed by others. Within thirty years, the basic balance sheet of photosynthesis had been established by a number of scientists, including the Dutch physician Jan Ingenhousz, and two Swiss, Jean Senebier and Nicolas Théodore de Saussure. The observation that mint could restore oxygen to an atmosphere from which this gas had been removed was confirmed and extended to other plants. Senebier, in 1783, found that only the green parts of plants possessed the ability to produce oxygen. Moreover, Ingenhousz had already shown that the formation of oxygen occurred only in the presence of sunlight. Ingenhousz's experiment also made clear the fact that in this process of adding oxygen to the air, plants simultaneously extracted another gaseous material, a substance we now know as carbon dioxide. In addition to the exchange of gases with the surrounding air, there was the growth of the plant itself. In 1804, de Saussure showed that plants consumed carbon dioxide in the production of organic material and oxygen. The plant gained considerable weight during the process. It was later established that the overall gain in plant weight, together with the weight of the oxygen given off, equalled the weight of all the raw materials consumed by the plant. These raw materials consisted partly of the carbon dioxide removed from the air but largely of water, incorporated by the plant through a number of very complex chemical processes. We can consider all of these light-induced changes as a definition of photosynthesis.

Green Plants as Chemical Factories

Photosynthesis can be summarized in the following word equation:

$$\text{carbon dioxide} + \text{water} \longrightarrow \text{oxygen} + \text{sugar} \qquad (1)$$

The raw materials are on the left-hand side of the arrow and the end products are on the right. Of the many plant compounds, only sugar is indicated, because it is the primary product of carbon-dioxide assimilation.

The same equation can be expressed in chemical shorthand as follows:

$$CO_2 + H_2O \longrightarrow O_2 + \{CH_2O\} \qquad (2)$$

The chemical formulas CO_2, H_2O and O_2, of course, give the number of atoms of carbon (C), hydrogen (H) or oxygen (O) in one molecule of carbon dioxide, water and oxygen gas respectively. The formula in brackets is the *empirical formula* of sugar. That is, $\{CH_2O\}$ indicates the correct *ratio* of carbon, hydrogen, and oxygen atoms in the compound, but it does not show the actual number of atoms in one molecule of sugar. There is a whole group of plant sugars, all consisting only of carbon, hydrogen, and oxygen. Their molecular formulas are different, but the ratio of carbon to hydrogen to oxygen in most of them is 1 to 2 to 1, or $\{CH_2O\}$.

The CO_2 required for photosynthesis by land plants is absorbed from the atmosphere, and by aquatic plants from the surrounding water. Water is supplied to the leaves of higher plants through their root systems. In aquatic plants, there is direct penetration of water from the surroundings into the photosynthetic tissues. Some of the sugar produced is quickly used in various biochemical processes of the plant.

Larger amounts are stored as starch. Because the conversion of sugar to starch does not depend directly on light, it is not included in the overall equation for photosynthesis. Similarly, the formation of fats and proteins is not shown since they, too, are secondary products.

It is important to note that in photosynthesis organic matter is formed entirely from *inorganic* substances. Both carbon dioxide and water are inorganic (i.e., mineral) substances. Sugar, on the other hand, is a typical *organic* substance, occurring in living organisms. It was once thought that the more complicated carbon-containing compounds could be produced only in living cells; hence the term "organic." Today, although such compounds can often be made synthetically in the laboratory, they are still called organic compounds because they are so characteristic of living things. As a rule, naturally occurring inorganic compounds are perfectly stable. But most

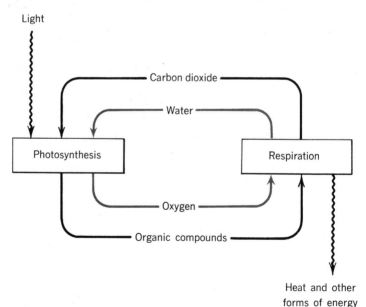

Fig. 1-1. Photosynthesis uses light energy to convert carbon dioxide and water into organic compounds and oxygen. In respiration this process is reversed, with energy as one of the products.

organic compounds are relatively unstable and are eventually broken down by organic decay or other processes. Every living cell, whether plant or animal, can perform many chemical reactions in which one organic compound is converted into another. It is mainly by photosynthesis, however, that large quantities of organic matter are made from inorganic compounds.

We can better appreciate the special character of photosynthesis by writing Equation (2) in reverse:

$$\{CH_2O\} + O_2 \longrightarrow CO_2 + H_2O \qquad (3)$$

Equation (3) represents the combustion of sugar with oxygen of the air to form carbon dioxide and water. This process, known as *respiration,* occurs not only in animal cells but in plant cells as well. At night, when a plant does not photosynthesize, there is a net depletion of organic matter as a result of respiration. In the daylight hours, both photosynthesis and respiration occur simultaneously in plants. During an active growing period, however, the rate of photosynthesis may be as much as 30 times greater than the rate of resipration. The net effect in a growing plant, therefore, is an accumulation of sugar and other organic compounds. Figure 1–1 illustrates the roles of photosynthesis and respiration in the biological world.

The total amount of organic compounds formed each year by photosynthesizing plants has been estimated at more than 100 billion tons. Well over half of this amount—perhaps as much as 85 percent—is produced by *phytoplankton,* minute plants living near the surface of the oceans (Figure 1–2). The plant kingdom as a whole is by far the largest chemical "factory" on our planet. Although some of this yield is lost in respiration and decay, what remains serves as the primary organic food for the entire animal kingdom. Some of the materials produced by plants, such as wood and fibers, are used by man for purposes other than food. Other organic materials are converted by slow decay processes into petroleum and coal.

A biochemical operation of this magnitude would quickly deplete the earth's atmosphere of its CO_2 if there were no compensating process. Even if all the dissolved forms of CO_2

in the oceans were added to the amount in the air, green plants could remove the total in 300 to 400 years. The fact that our atmosphere still contains CO_2 means that this gas is being returned to the atmosphere by equally large-scale processes. Nature has arranged her economy so that the rate of CO_2 consumption in photosynthesis is just about balanced by the rate of restoration of CO_2. Respiration in plants and animals is responsible for most of the restoration of atmospheric CO_2, in accordance with Equation (3), supplemented by the decay of organic matter and by the burning of fuels. As a result, the average surface concentration of CO_2 in the air, about 0.03 percent, has remained practically constant for thousands of years. The set of processes maintaining the CO_2 balance, known as the *carbon cycle,* is important not only in maintain-

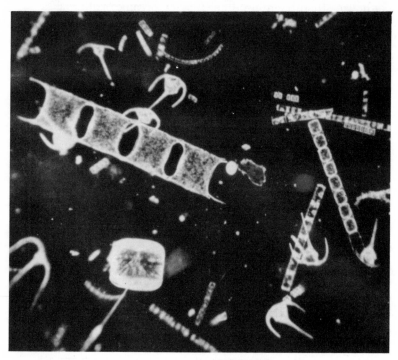

Woods Hole Oceanographic Institution

Fig. 1-2.   Phytoplankton.

ing a constant chemical environment in the atmosphere, but also in regulating the surface temperature of the earth, since atmospheric CO_2 helps to reduce the loss of heat from the earth to outer space.

Photosynthesis is also important in regulating the oxygen content of the atmosphere. It has been estimated that the current planet-wide rate of photosynthesis is such as to produce, in just several thousand years, the entire oxygen content of the atmosphere (about a thousand million million tons). As in the case of CO_2, the concentration of atmospheric oxygen is also believed to have been maintained at its present value for a very long period of time, as a result of a state of balance in the *oxygen cycle*. Many scientists who have studied the geological history of the earth believe that there was practically no oxygen in the atmosphere until the first photosynthesizing plants evolved. If this view is correct, then the emergence of photosynthesis as a life process played a crucial role in paving the way for other forms of life. Photosynthetic oxygen was essential for the emergence of animal life dependent on respiration for its very existence.

The appearance of oxygen in the atmosphere had another beneficial effect on biological evolution. Oxygen in the upper atmosphere interacts with some of the ultraviolet radiation coming from the sun to form ozone. Ozone is a gas that differs from normal oxygen in having three atoms of oxygen per molecule instead of two. Although ozone has a disagreeable odor and is, in fact, injurious to most living organisms, the ozone layer in the upper atmosphere is essential to the existence of life on our planet. It acts as a screen to prevent the sun's ultraviolet radiation from reaching the surface of the earth. It can do this because it has the special property, not possessed by the major atmospheric gases, of being able to absorb particular kinds of ultraviolet rays that are especially harmful to all living cells. Without this ozone layer, the surface of the earth would be constantly irradiated with these very harmful rays, and most forms of surface life could not survive. This is a second reason for believing that primitive photosynthesizing plants had to precede the evolution of complex organisms.

Variations in the Photosynthetic Process

In addition to the main course of photosynthesis, summarized in Equation (2), some alternate processes have developed. The common feature of these variant forms is the conversion of CO_2 into organic compounds *without* the production of oxygen gas. In the early 1930's, C. B. van Niel of Stanford University proposed the following scheme for representing such variations in the overall equation:

$$CO_2 + 2H_2A \longrightarrow \{CH_2O\} + 2A + H_2O$$

where H_2A is an oxidizable molecule (e.g., isopropyl alcohol) and A is one of the products of oxidation (e.g., acetone; for a discussion of *oxidation,* see Chapter 6).

Most of the dozens of known examples of this sort are found in the green and the purple *photosynthetic bacteria.* Very often these bacteria live in muds, out of contact with the atmosphere, and have adapted themselves to an *anaerobic* (airless) way of life. The layer of mud covering the bacteria is, of course, not so thick as to prevent the necessary amount of light from reaching them. Among the best known examples of this kind are the *sulfur bacteria,* so named because they produce sulfur as one of the end products of photosynthesis. This process, as formulated by van Niel, is what one would expect from the preceding equation:

$$CO_2 + 2H_2S \longrightarrow \{CH_2O\} + 2S + H_2O$$

The particular compound that supplies the hydrogen needed to form sugar is hydrogen sulfide, H_2S. This gas, well known for its characteristic rotten-egg odor, occurs naturally in sulfur springs and active volcanoes. It is also made by certain nonphotosynthetic bacteria in the decomposition of some common inorganic, sulfur-containing minerals. Sulfur bacteria may accumulate their sulfur as small droplets of the pure element or they may even convert it to sulfuric acid! In other photosynthetic bacteria, the reaction may require one of a variety of chemicals, including hydrogen gas, fats, alcohols, and acids. Some of these substances are organic compounds and the photosynthetic bacteria that require them cannot exist in a completely inorganic environment, as can green plants or the sulfur bacteria.

Some green algae adapt themselves to perform a bacterial type of photosynthesis if they are deprived of oxygen for a sufficient period of time. The chemical variation most thoroughly studied in such adapted algae is called *photoreduction.* The reaction was discovered in the early 1930's by Hans Gaffron, in Germany (now at Florida State University). Photoreduction involves the conversion of hydrogen gas to water and the simultaneous formation of organic compounds from CO_2:

$$CO_2 + 2H_2 \longrightarrow \{CH_2O\} + H_2O$$

These variations of photosynthesis in bacteria and algae, however, play an insignificant role in the production of organic material, when compared with the most common form of photosynthesis performed by green plants. Nevertheless, the occurrence of alternate photosynthetic schemes is an interesting example of biological adaptation to special environmental conditions, such as the lack of oxygen or the accumulation of certain chemicals, like H_2S, that are normally poisonous to living matter. The differences in the chemical course of photosynthesis pose an interesting question to the scientific investigator: What part or parts of the photosynthetic process, if any, are common to all types of photosynthesis? The methods of comparative biochemistry are applicable here. Points of similarity and difference help to shed light on the probable evolutionary history of living forms and to indicate the minimum number of essential steps in this complicated life process.

Photosynthesis as a Photochemical Process

Photochemistry, the study of the influence of light on chemical reactions, is a fairly broad branch of chemistry. Tens of thousands of photochemical reactions are known, but relatively few of them are observed in the biological world. The exposure to light of photographic film in a camera is probably the most familiar example. The making of a blueprint from a draftsman's drawing is another. The irradiation of milk to increase its vitamin-D content involves a series of photochemical reactions. Organic chemists often use light to produce a reaction different from the one that would have taken place in the dark. Many photochemical reactions are destructive, and this is why many chemicals, including drugs, are stored in brown bottles that are opaque to damaging ultraviolet radiation.

Among the many known photochemical reactions, however, photosynthesis occupies a special role. Aside from the fact that it represents the largest-scale chemical process on our planet, photosynthesis is one of the very few photochemical reactions in which light energy is converted to chemical energy with high efficiency. This aspect will be taken up in greater detail in the next chapter, where the nature of light energy and chemical energy is discussed.

An even more unusual aspect of photosynthesis is that its high efficiency is maintained in spite of the great complexity of the process. The production of one oxygen molecule requires at least a dozen successive chemical reactions. The actual number may be much greater. Nature has endowed green plants with a scheme for directing traffic, as it were, so that these different individual steps occur in the proper sequence. Some steps require the products of an earlier step. Others involve the products from several of the earlier steps, all at one time. The efficient conversion of light to chemical energy in a process as complicated as photosynthesis is indeed unmatched in all of photochemistry.

The plan of this book is to examine in detail some of the individual steps occurring in photosynthesis and to give examples of the methods used for identifying and studying them.

2

Photosynthesis as Energy Conversion

In Chapter 1 we discussed some of the chemical changes that occur in photosynthesis. In this chapter, we shall focus our attention on the energy changes that occur in the process. The *photo* in "photosynthesis" refers, of course, to light, one of the many forms of energy; and *synthesis* involves another form of energy, chemical energy.

The Nature of Light

For several centuries it has been known that light is a wave phenomenon. The wave nature of light accounts for *refraction* (the bending of light when it passes from one medium to another) and for *interference* (the separation of light into alternate regions of light and dark when light beams coming from several closely spaced points are combined). Roughly speaking, the technical term *wave* refers to a physical disturbance that varies regularly with time. In an ocean wave, this disturbance appears as the rise and fall at the surface of the water. In the case of a light wave, there is a regular increase and decrease in the intensity of the minute electrical and magnetic fields that constitute the wave. (Like X rays and radio waves, visible light is a form of electromagnetic energy.)

An important property of any wave is its wavelength, the distance between two successive peaks. Wavelengths of many feet may separate two ocean-wave crests, but the wavelengths of visible light are less than a millionth of a meter. It is convenient to use a special unit of length called the *Angstrom unit*, or *Å*, in describing the wavelengths of visible light. One Å is equal to one hundred-millionth of a centimeter (or about 250 million Angstroms per inch).

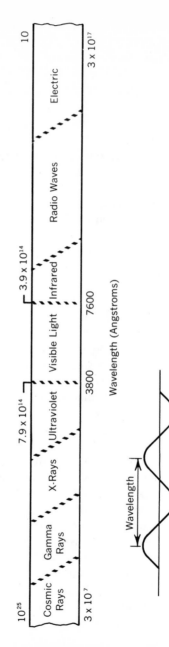

Fig. 2-1. Electromagnetic spectrum ranges from electrical waves to cosmic rays. Note that frequency is inversely proportional to wavelength. As shown in the drawing at lower left, wavelength is defined as the distance between the peaks of two successive waves.

White light is a mixture of waves of different wavelengths. These different components can be separated into a spectrum by passing light through a prism or diffraction grating. The visible portion of the electromagnetic spectrum runs from the violet, at about 4000Å, to the red, at about 7500Å. Infrared, above 7500Å, and ultraviolet radiation, below 4000Å, are natural extensions of the electromagnetic spectrum that our eyes cannot see. (See Fig. 2–1.)

It is quite easy to find examples showing that light is a form of energy and can therefore be converted into other forms of energy: A black object is heated when exposed to light—light energy is converted into thermal energy, or heat. The active metal surface of a photoelectric cell ejects electrons when exposed to light—here light energy is converted into the energy of motion, or kinetic energy, of the electron. The sensitive surface of a photographer's light meter develops a voltage and causes a deflection of the meter needle when exposed to light—light energy is converted into electrical energy.

An important part of our understanding of light as an energy-carrier came from studies of the *photoelectric effect*. This effect, applied in such familiar devices as automatic-door controls and burglar alarms, is basically the ejection of an electron from a metal when light strikes the metal (see Fig. 2–2). It has been known since the end of the nineteenth century that a strong beam of light causes the ejection of more electrons than does a weak beam, but some wavelengths of light do not produce the photoelectric effect at all, no matter how intense the beam. The wavelength must be less than a certain limiting value that is specific for each metal. For some metals the critical wavelength lies in the visible region (e.g., 6600 Å for cesium), and for others it lies in the ultraviolet region (e.g., 2600 Å for tungsten).

In 1905, Albert Einstein provided an explanation of the puzzling photoelectric phenomenon. Einstein proposed that light energy is transmitted not in a continuous stream but only in individual units, or *quanta*. The term *quantum* had been introduced just five years earlier by the German physicist Max Planck. Planck had advanced the hypothesis that the transfer

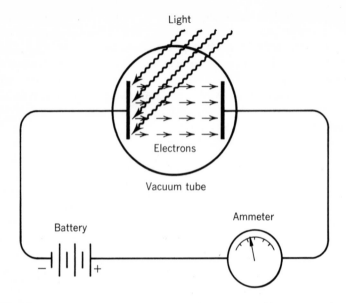

Fig. 2-2. Photoelectric effect: Electrons are ejected from the surface of a metal when light strikes the metal. The frequency of the light must be greater than a certain minimum value.

of radiation energy within a hot object involved discrete "packets" of energy—quanta. According to this hypothesis, the energy of a single quantum could be calculated from the equation

$$E = h\nu$$

where E is the energy, h is a constant (known as *Planck's constant*), and ν is the frequency of the particular electromagnetic radiation in question.

It is clear from the equation that the greater the frequency of the radiation, the greater the energy. That is, the energy is *directly proportional* to the frequency. Now frequency is *indirectly proportional* to wavelength. The shorter the wavelength, therefore, the greater the energy, and vice versa. For example, X rays are more energetic and have a higher frequency and a shorter wavelength than do radio waves.

What Einstein did was to extend Planck's hypothesis to include light. Thus all light quanta of a given wavelength (i.e., frequency) have exactly the same amount of energy. Light quanta of different wavelengths carry different amounts of energy. The relationship between energy per quantum and wavelength, as we just saw, is one of inverse proportionality—*the longer the wavelength, the smaller the amount of energy per quantum.*

Now the minimum amount of energy needed to eject an electron from a particular metal is a characteristic of that metal. Consequently, when a quantum of light strikes a metal, a photoelectron is produced only if the energy of the quantum is at least equal to the "critical energy" of the metal. Einstein also postulated that all the energy of a single light quantum (or *photon,* as it is more familiarly known) is transferred to a single electron. In other words, one quantum will never transfer its energy to two or more electrons. Conversely, the energy of two or more quanta can never be combined to eject one electron. This one-to-one relationship between a light quantum and a particle of matter applies to molecules in photochemistry as well as to electrons in the photoelectric effect. The principle that one quantum of light can bring about a direct photochemical change in exactly one molecule is known as Einstein's Law of Photochemistry.

Chemicals as Energy-storing Devices

Chemical substances may be thought of as energy-storing devices. By "energy-storer" is meant a system that is capable of assuming a more stable chemical form. In its natural tendency to achieve greater stability, such a system will lose the chemical energy it has stored, releasing it in some other form. A charge of TNT is an example of a chemical substance whose atoms are not in their most stable arrangement. When detonated, the TNT explodes and the component carbon, hydrogen, nitrogen, and oxygen atoms are rearranged into more stable combinations. The resulting compounds, including oxides of carbon, water, and nitrogen gas, are said to contain less chemical energy than the original TNT. The energy re-

leased during the "rearrangement" appears largely as heat and
mechanical energy of the explosion. It is important to note
that whereas high-energy chemicals can be converted to low-
energy chemicals, the reverse process never takes place *spontaneously.*

The forces that determine the relative stability of different
combinations of atoms are known as *chemical forces,* and the
link between atoms held together by chemical forces is called
a *chemical bond.* Chemical forces between neighboring atoms
can be enormous, over a billion billion billion billion times
greater than the force of gravitational attraction between the
same two atoms. Whereas the gravitational attraction between
two particles depends only on their masses and the distance
between them, chemical forces depend on the types of atoms
in a given compound. This makes possible atomic combinations of widely different bond strengths, or stability.

Figure 2–3 illustrates the difference in stability of two hypo-
thetical combinations of four atoms, represented by two small
and two large circles. Assume that the energy E_B of combination B is greater than E_A, the energy of combination A. If
there were some way of forcing the atoms of B to rearrange
themselves on command into A, the difference in energy
$(E_B - E_A)$ would be released as heat or some other form of
energy during the rearrangement. This is exactly what happens
with chemical fuels like gasoline, natural gas, or coal. The
particular combinations of carbon and hydrogen atoms in the
fuel and the molecules of oxygen in the air that support the
combustion would together represent a high-energy state, like
B in Figure 2–3. On ignition of the mixture, the atoms rearrange so as to form a lower-energy combination such as A.
In the case of these fuels, the products of the combustion are
mostly water and CO_2. Depending on the design of the burner,
the energy yield of the process may appear as heat, as
mechanical motion of a motor, or as electrical output of a fuel
cell. The actual diagrams of the atomic combinations are, of
course, much more complicated than those shown in Figure
2–3, but the principle of rearrangement of atoms to form combinations of lower energy is the same.

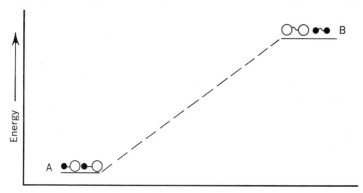

Fig. 2-3. Change of atomic combination changes the energy state. High-energy combinations tend to revert to low-energy ones.

What has been said so far about the release of heat or some other form of energy when a high-energy chemical arrangement is changed to a lower-energy one raises an obvious question about the effect of the speed of the reaction on the amount of energy released. Sometimes the change is very rapid, in which case we call it an explosion. Often the change can be controlled, and we speak of a burning process in the case of fuels. In other instances, the change may be a slow, drawn-out affair, as in the decay of a dead tree in a forest. The actual total amount of energy released, however, is always the same for a given chemical change, regardless of the speed.

The animal world, of which mankind is but a part, needs energy to sustain life and to grow. Each individual has built into itself a kind of a combination furnace and motor, so designed that the energy released when high-energy chemicals change into low-energy forms can be used directly for all of that individual's needs. Some of the purposes for which the human body requires energy (released in respiration) are the maintenance of body heat, muscular motion, and the synthesis of many types of chemicals that the body needs to function properly. The sources of energy-yielding chemicals are the fats, proteins, and carbohydrates in the food we eat. The importance of the energy content of our food is reflected in the fact that the basic unit for measuring the amounts of these foods is the *Calorie*, a unit of energy.

In terms of energy, the fats, proteins, and carbohydrates we consume, together with the oxygen we breathe, correspond to a high-energy level, like B in Figure 2–3. The chemistry of the body converts these materials into lower-energy forms, like A in Figure 2–3. These end-products are mostly CO_2 and water, with some simple nitrogen compounds, and are eventually returned to the atmosphere and to the system of the world's rivers and oceans. Animals alone are unable to reverse the cycle, to take carbon dioxide, water, and nitrogen from the atmosphere and the oceans, and convert them once again into high-energy food-fuels. For this reversal, animals are dependent on the plant kingdom.

Energy Pumping by Green Plants

Plants have a special built-in apparatus for converting low-energy raw materials into foods. Any scheme for doing this requires some kind of energy, and it corresponds to "pumping" the atoms uphill from level A to level B in the preceding example. The energy source of plants is radiant energy from the sun. The plant apparatus that absorbs sunlight and, of course, converts solar energy into chemical energy is the *photosynthetic apparatus*. Photosynthesis may be thought of as a light-driven chemical pump, pumping atoms from low-energy arrangements to high-energy forms that can be stored.

Photosynthesis is unique in this respect even among photochemical reactions. Most photochemical reactions do not store energy at all, they simply speed up the rate of conversion of one chemical combination into another combination having an equal or smaller amount of chemical energy. Among those photochemical reactions in which energy is stored, the overall efficiency is very low in practically every case. The reason for this is that newly formed high-energy compounds are often so unstable that they do not survive long enough to be useful energy storers. There is a definite probability that their atoms will undergo spontaneous rearrangements and form the original low-energy compounds. One simple example is provided by iodine. When an iodine molecule (I_2) absorbs blue or near-ultraviolet light, it breaks up into two iodine atoms. The separated iodine atoms represent a higher state of chemical energy than the I_2 molecule. Temporarily, then, light energy has been stored as chemical energy. In a vessel containing only iodine, however, the atoms will quickly unite in pairs to re-form I_2 molecules, thus undoing the energy-storing work of the light. The special trick of Nature in photosynthesis is to prevent the high-energy primary products of the photochemical reaction from undergoing a rapid back-reaction, which would waste the energy-storing achievement and restore the starting materials to their initial state.

How much energy is stored during photosynthesis? We can answer this question from several points of view. For each gram of CO_2 converted to sugar during photosynthesis, about 2.5 kilocalories of energy are stored. (A kilocalorie is the same as a food Calorie—the amount of heat necessary to raise the temperature of 10 grams of liquid water 100 centigrade degrees.) Some plants, while doubling their own weight in a sunny 12-hour day, convert an amount of CO_2 equal to about 25 percent of their initial weight. Thus, in one day, a plant weighing 100 grams would store over 60 kilocalories as photosynthetic products by evening, and would then weigh 200 grams. It has been estimated that in one year the world's plants store more than one billion billion kilocalories in the form of photosynthetic products. This total corresponds to the fuel value of one million million barrels of gasoline.

Photosynthesis is thus a crucial factor in the earth's annual energy budget. In addition, we are taking advantage of the photosynthetic energy storage of past geologic ages when we use natural chemical fuels to operate power plants, motors, and furnaces. Wood is a direct photosynthetic storage product of plants. The so-called fossil fuels, including natural gas, petroleum, and coal, are decomposition products of the photosynthetic activity of earlier periods in the history of our planet. The only important non-photosynthetic primary energy sources used by man are water power and nuclear power.

3

Experimental Measurements
of Photosynthesis

The consideration of energy conversion in the last chapter leads naturally to the question of how this conversion is measured in plants. Indeed, some understanding of the methods employed in the investigation of photosynthetic activity is essential if one is to gain more than a superficial grasp of the overall process.

Photosynthetic activity can be observed experimentally in any green plant; and a variety of methods have been developed to determine the rate of photosynthesis, the quantity of substances consumed and produced, and the particular compounds involved in the various reactions. For example, one can measure the amount of oxygen evolved, the amount of CO_2 consumed, or the amount of organic matter synthesized. But regardless of the method chosen, it is essential that the measurements be precise and that the experimental conditions be reproducible.

The Choice of Plant Material

Most of the early studies of photosynthesis were made with the leaves of higher plants. Leaves, however, have certain disadvantages for quantitative measurements. For one thing, it is hard to obtain leaves that are uniform in size and shape, even if the plants from which they are obtained are grown under controlled greenhouse conditions. Secondly, the very shape of the leaf makes it awkward to insert into many kinds of measuring instruments. Thirdly, the leaf itself is a very complex organ, consisting of several different kinds of tissues and cells;

and only the green cells of the leaf perform photosynthesis. Consequently, it is quite difficult to control the conditions under which photosynthesis takes place in these cells.

Shortly after World War I, the German biochemist Otto Warburg began a series of experiments that revolutionized the use of plant material for experiments on photosynthesis. He used water suspensions of *Chlorella,* a hardy genus of single-celled green algae found in most parts of the world (Fig. 3–1). Since then, several strains of *Chlorella* have been the favorite choice of most workers, for they can be grown in any laboratory under fairly standard conditions. The usual method of culturing *Chlorella* is to suspend a few cells in a nutrient medium containing the minerals required for growth. A stream

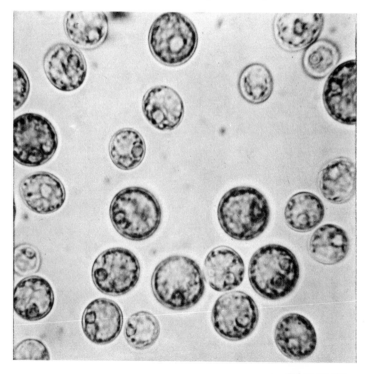

Robert W. Krauss

Fig. 3-1.   Single-celled algae of the genus **Chlorella.**

of air containing several percent CO_2 is bubbled through the suspension, which is illuminated by a suitable lamp. Almost any lamp that does not produce deep-ultraviolet light is suitable. The algae will, under favorable conditions, double their weight, and the number of cells, in 10 hours. At this rate of growth, a suspension that is initially colorless to the eye will turn almost black-green in about four days.

One important advantage of using algae in research is the uniformity of the cells. This is not to say that the individual cells are all alike. But because the cells are so small and so many are used in a single experiment (several million cells per cubic centimeter in a typical suspension), their differences average out and the laws of statistics can be applied to such a large sampling. Another convenience of working with unicellular algae is that the suspensions can be treated as though they were true solutions. The algae do not settle out rapidly. Moreover, they can be easily poured and portioned out, even with a pipette.

Determining the Rate of Photosynthesis

Most determinations of the rate of photosynthesis have involved measurements of gas pressure. A suspension of algae is placed in a closed vessel of known volume (see Fig. 3–2). When illuminated, the algae produce oxygen gas by photosynthesis and the total pressure of the gas in the apparatus increases. Conversely, when the light is turned off, the algae consume CO_2 by respiration, and the pressure decreases. The pressure readings show that the consumption of CO_2 during the light period does not balance the pressure increase due to oxygen production. The explanation is that CO_2 is highly soluble in water. The algae can therefore take a large fraction of their CO_2 directly from the solution instead of from the gas volume. The pressure is thus little affected by the consumption of CO_2 (or, similarly, by CO_2 given off during the "dark period.") The total pressure, indicated by the fluid level of a manometer attached to the vessel, is measured at regular intervals. If, in addition, the temperature, the liquid and gas volumes of the vessel, and the solubilities of the gases are known, the exact rate of photosynthesis can be calculated.

A specific method for measuring the oxygen evolved in photosynthesis is the *polarographic method*. In this procedure a leaf or a thin film of algae is pressed against a strip of plati-

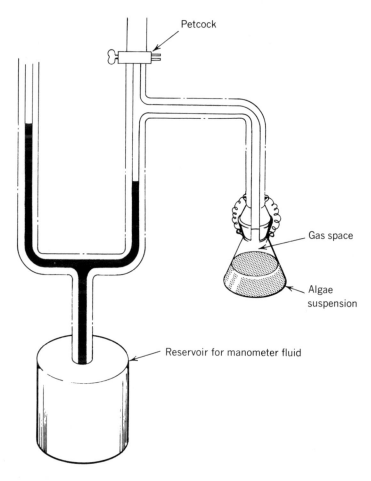

Fig. 3-2. Typical manometer arrangement used in gas-pressure experiments. Evolution of oxygen or carbon dioxide by the algae produces a corresponding change in the levels of the fluid.

num, which serves as an electrode. A second metal electrode is immersed in the fluid bathing the algae sample. A voltage is then applied between the two electrodes. The changes observed in the electrical current are proportional to changes in the rate of oxygen production (in the light) or consumption (in the dark) by the algae. Polarography is faster than the gas-pressure method—one-tenth of a second as compared to one minute (see Fig. 3–3).

To describe fully all methods employed in determining the rate of photosynthesis would take volumes. We shall mention briefly only a few others. Since solutions of CO_2 are acidic,

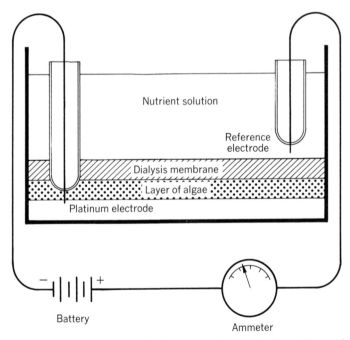

Fig. 3-3. Polarographic method. A layer of algae is allowed to settle on a flat platinum electrode and is then covered with a dialysis membrane such as cellophane. A nutrient solution is added. If a negative potential of about one volt is applied to the platinum electrode, the excess current in the completed circuit is proportional to the rate of oxygen production of the algae.

the amount of acidity can be measured to determine the rate of production or consumption of CO_2 in solution. Also, the ability of a gas to conduct heat can be measured as an index of both the oxygen and carbon dioxide of a gas stream. Because the CO_2 absorbs infrared radiation of a particular wavelength, the concentration of CO_2 in a gas stream can be monitored continuously by an infrared spectrometer. A mass spectrometer, which discriminates among molecules of different mass, can be used for the analysis of both O_2 and CO_2 in a gas. In addition, photosynthetic activity can be measured by the methods of radioisotope research, if the CO_2 contains radioactive carbon. These last two methods will be discussed in Chapters 5 and 6.

The Use and Measurement of Light

In photosynthesis experiments it is extremely important to control the quality and the intensity of the light. The term *quality* refers to wavelength. In photosynthesis, the most effective light is the visible part of the spectrum. (Light in the near-infrared region, up to 9000Å, can also be used by the photosynthetic bacteria.) In nature, plants must use whatever portion of the sun's visible radiation they can get. In the laboratory, however, there is a choice. Either filament or fluorescent lamps may be used. Both supply light of many wavelengths. Particular portions of the spectrum can be selected, if desired, by the use of filters. Even colored transparent wrapping paper is sometimes used for this purpose.

The intensity of light is expressed in a number of ways. Perhaps the most familiar units of illumination are those used in photography, the *foot-candle* and the *meter-candle*. These units are especially useful for describing natural daylight, and the same type of light meter used by a photographer may be used for a laboratory or field experiment. For artificial light, however, especially when a specific wavelength is being used, more elaborate methods are needed. Often the intensity is expressed in energy units, such as ergs or calories per square centimeter per second. (For example, the intensity of solar radiation at the top of the earth's atmosphere is usually given

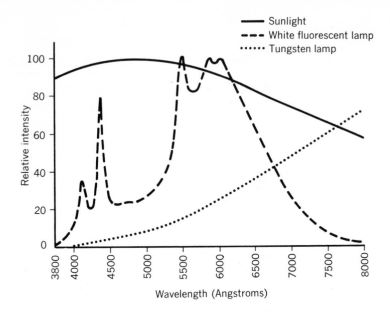

Fig. 3-4. Spectral distributions of three light sources. The relative intensity at any wavelength is given as a percentage of the maximum intensity (at one wavelength) for the particular source.

as 1.9 calories per minute per square centimeter of earth surface for vertical exposure.) There are instruments that directly measure the intensity of a light beam and respond equally well at all wavelengths. The most common of these is the *thermopile*, which converts incident radiation into electrical energy, which in turn can easily be measured. Even photochemical reactions are sometimes used as light detectors, in devices known as *actinometers*.

A light source is also often described by its spectral distribution, which gives the relative intensity at each wavelength. Figure 3–4 shows the distribution curves for several light sources.

4

Limiting Factors in Photosynthesis

There is no simple answer to the question of how much photosynthesis a given plant performs. There are many different answers, depending on conditions. Diseased plants, as would be expected, do not perform as well as healthy plants. Even in healthy plant cells, however, the actual amount of photosynthetic activity depends on many factors, including the light intensity, the quality of the light, the concentration of carbon dioxide, the temperature, the previous history of light and darkness, the availability of a host of mineral nutrients, and the presence or absence of certain inhibitory substances.

The Saturation Curve

What is the relationship between the rate of photosynthesis and light intensity? The most clear-cut answer to this question is based on experiments performed with suspensions of algae. Figure 4–1 summarizes a number of experimental measurements of photosynthetic activity in *Chlorella* suspensions. The curves reveal the effect of light intensity on photosynthesis under three different sets of conditions, A, B, and C. The carbon-dioxide concentration and temperature in each experiment are given on the next page. As the figure shows, the most favorable conditions in terms of carbon-dioxide concentration and temperature are those of Experiment A.

Note that curve A in Figure 4–1 is a straight line at the lower light intensities. In this region, designated as x, the rate of photosynthesis is directly proportional to the light intensity. This is known as the *light-limiting region.* Here all the light absorbed is used for photosynthesis and the rate of photosynthesis is limited only by the availability of light.

At the highest intensities, the curve becomes a horizontal line. In this region, y, the photosynthetic rate reaches a plateau and increases no further even when the intensity of light is increased. This region is called the *saturation region,* because the maximum capacity to photosynthetize has been reached, or "saturated." Therefore factors other than light intensity must be responsible for limiting the rate of photosynthesis at saturation. In the intermediate region, where the curve is bending, the rate of photosynthesis must be limited partly by the availability of light and partly by other factors.

Curve A shows that there must be at least two different steps in photosynthesis—a photochemical step, requiring light,

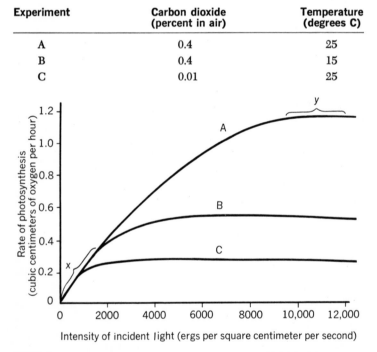

Experiment	Carbon dioxide (percent in air)	Temperature (degrees C)
A	0.4	25
B	0.4	15
C	0.01	25

Fig. 4-1. Typical saturation curves obtained in three separate experiments (see table). The light-limiting region is indicated by **x**; the saturation region, by **y**.

and a non-photochemical step. The rate of the former depends on light intensity, but the rate of the latter does not. If the two steps occur in sequence, the overall rate is determined by whichever is slower. This is the familiar principle of the bucket brigade. If every man but one in a chain requires 30 seconds to pass a bucket to his neighbor, and if the one exception requires 60 seconds, the overall rate of moving buckets through the chain will be one bucket every 60 seconds. This is true regardless of the position of the "slowpoke" in the chain. So long as the slowest man requires 60 seconds, no advantage is gained if the others improve their time from 30 seconds to, say, 20 seconds. So it must be in photosynthesis. At lower light intensities, the photochemical step is the slow step and the overall rate can be improved by speeding it up. At higher light intensities, however, the photochemical step is so rapid, compared to the non-photochemical step, that no further increase in the overall rate is to be gained from making the photochemical step still faster. It should also be pointed out that one cannot tell from this type of experiment which step comes first in the chain of reactions.

Light Limitations

In the light-limiting region, x, the percentage of absorbed light actually used in photochemical reactions reaches a maximum. Here the dark, or non-photochemical, reactions are so rapid, in comparison, that there is little chance of the absorbed light's being wasted. Therefore questions about the most efficient use of light can be answered by experimental measurements in the x region.

Exactly how many quanta of light must be absorbed in order to produce one molecule of oxygen in photosynthesis? Experiments have shown that in green algae, such as *Chlorella*, the number of light quanta required does not depend very much on wavelength. This number, known as the *quantum requirement* of photosynthesis, is apparently more significant than the amount of energy absorbed. A quantum of red light at 6850Å can be as effective as a quantum of blue light at 4200Å, which carries 63 percent more energy. (Remember that the energy of a quantum is inversely proportional to its wavelength.) The lowest-energy quantum that can be efficiently used by *Chlorella* has been found by experiment to have a wavelength of 6850Å. The average value of the minimum quantum requirement from many experiments is close to 8. Therefore, since Einstein's Law of Photochemistry states that only one quantum can be used at a time in a photochemical reaction, we can conclude from the requirement of eight quanta that eight photochemical events are involved in the production of one oxygen molecule.

What is the maximum fraction of light energy that is converted to chemical energy in photosynthesis? The answer to this question requires the measurement of two quantities: the amount of chemical energy stored in sugar and oxygen during the photosynthetic process, and the amount of light energy needed to do the job. The first of these quantities is determined by measuring the amount of heat produced when a known amount of sugar is converted to CO_2 and water (by oxidation; Equation (3) in Chapter 1). The second quantity is determined from the measurement of the amount of light absorbed during a period of photosynthesis long enough to produce exactly the same weight of sugar. The results of these measurements show that 35 percent of the absorbed energy at 6850Å is changed to chemical energy. This is a high degree of efficiency, even by the standards of modern power plants. No other photochemical process comes at all close to this value.

How much light is needed to reach the plateau, or saturation rate, of photosynthesis? For most plants, intensities of white light amounting to 2000 foot-candles are sufficient to reach the highest observed rates. This is less than the intensity of sunlight at noon on a bright day in the temperate zones. That is to say, the green plants on the earth's surface can get enough sunlight to satisfy their maximum needs during the bright part of a clear day. This, of course, would not be true for plants growing close together in a dense forest, for example, where the taller trees act as light screens for the shorter ones, nor for ocean plants far below the surface of the water. Plants growing at depths of 25 meters, even in perfectly clear water, receive visible light of an intensity less than one-third the value at the surface and can no longer photosynthesize at the maximum rate.

Limiting Factors in Dark Reactions

We have already shown that factors other than light are responsible for limiting the saturation rate of photosynthesis (region y of Figure 4–1). For lack of a better word, the particular reactions affected by these factors are called *dark reactions*. They are so named because, at any given concentration of the reactants, they proceed independently of the amount of light available to the plant—in the dark as well as in the light. These are the reactions that must precede or follow the true photochemical steps. The rate of the dark reactions can be decreased by various means, but it cannot be increased above a certain value by any factor that the experimenter can control.

One way of lowering the saturation rate is to lower the temperature. Curve B of Figure 4–1 shows the saturation rate at 15°C, 10°C below that in Experiment A. At light intensities above 2000 ergs per square centimeter per second, the photosynthetic rate is considerably less at the lower temperature. But at the very low intensities, the two rate curves are identical. This means that the reactions in the light-limiting region, like most true photochemical reactions, are not sensitive to temperature. On the other hand, the rate of ordinary chemical reactions, those not requiring light, usually decreases with decreasing temperature, as appears to be the case with the dark reactions. The optimum temperature for photosynthetic rates varies slightly from plant to plant but is normally between 25° and 30°C (77° to 86°F).

A second way of lowering the saturation rate is to reduce the concentration of CO_2 in the plant cells. Curve C of Figure 4–1 represents such a situation. Here again there is no influence on the rate at the lowest light intensities, where the photochemical step is the rate-limiting factor. The conclusion to be drawn, then, is that CO_2 does not participate directly in any photochemical reaction. For most plants, the optimum saturation rate of photosynthesis is reached at an atmospheric carbon-dioxide content of several tenths of one per cent (by volume). This figure is greater than the average carbon-dioxide content of the atmosphere, which is 0.03 percent in non-urban regions and up to 0.1 per cent in cities. In other words, most plants in their natural environment do not have enough carbon dioxide to make maximum use of light at high intensities.

Flashing-light Experiments

Even after selection of the optimum light intensity, temperature, and carbon-dioxide pressure, there remains a fundamental limitation to a plant's photosynthesizing capacity. This limitation is the minimum time required by the plant to complete the *slowest* dark reaction of the photosynthetic process. Like the slowest man in a bucket brigade, the slowest dark reaction is the basic rate-limiting factor (assuming that all other conditions are optimum). In 1932, two American biologists, Robert Emerson and William Arnold, performed an ingenious experiment in which they determined the period of the limiting dark reaction. Emerson and Arnold illuminated a sample of *Chlorella* with intense flashes of light that lasted less than one-thousandth of a second each. They repeated these flashes at regular intervals and measured the amount of photosynthesis over the course of hundreds of such cycles. By dividing the total amount of photosynthesis by the number of flashes, they calculated the average yield of photosynthesis per flash. Emerson and Arnold reasoned that they could improve the maximum yield per flash if they allowed sufficient time between flashes for the limiting dark reaction to run its course. The experiments confirmed their expectations.

Figure 4–2 summarizes the results of many such flashing-light experiments. For dark periods between flashes greater than about 0.06 second, the yield per flash is independent of

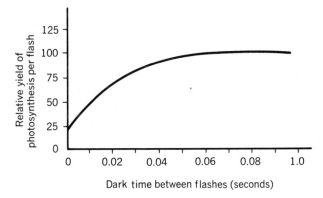

Fig. 4-2. Data from flashing-light experiments, summarized in this curve, show that the dark reaction that limits the rate of photosynthesis requires about 0.06 second for completion.

the dark time. For shorter dark times, the yield per flash decreases progressively. The conclusion is that the dark reaction determining the saturation rate of photosynthesis requires about 0.06 second for completion. The gently sloping shape of the curve shows that this dark reaction, like almost all chemical reactions, follows the statistical laws of random processes. In other words, identical chemical systems do not all undergo a reaction at the same instant but over a "spread-out" period. One would certainly expect to find such a "time spread" for a single reaction occurring in several million algae cells. Consequently, it is more correct to speak of the *average* rate of a reaction. The average dark time for this particular experiment has been computed to be about 0.02 second. This value, found in many experiments to vary between 0.01 and 0.02 second, is now considered to represent the average reaction time, in almost all green plants, for the essential step that limits the maximum rate of photosynthesis under optimum conditions of light intensity, temperature, and carbon-dioxide pressure.

It should be mentioned, in passing, that because photosynthesis is a process occurring in a living cell, anything that affects the health of the cell can affect photosynthesis. In addition to CO_2 and water, many other mineral ingredients, such as magnesium, nitrogen, phosphorus, and iron are needed in the nourishment of even the simplest cell. Without these minerals, plants cannot photosynthesize.

Manganese is something of an exception. Algae cultured without manganese sometimes retain a limited capacity for performing photochemical reactions, but not for normal photosynthesis. Such algae have been known to perform photoreduction, one of the variant types of photosynthesis in which CO_2 is assimilated but oxygen is not evolved. This has led experimenters to the conclusion that manganese plays a specific role in photosynthesis, particularly in one or two steps connected with oxygen evolution. Apparently the chemical reactions involving the incorporation of CO_2 are completely different from those involving the liberation of oxygen. In the next chapter, we will discuss other methods for unraveling the complete photosynthetic sequence.

5

The Pathway of Carbon
in Photosynthesis

We saw in the last chapter that a number of different steps must occur in the overall photosynthetic process. We examined the evidence showing that, in addition to the reactions occurring in the light, there is at least one dark reaction in which CO_2 is absorbed and at least one additional dark reaction whose rate depends only on factors within the living cell that are not subject to experimental control. Also, the reaction directly involving the uptake of CO_2 was found to be entirely different from the reaction in which oxygen gas is produced.

The above conclusions, although well established, hardly provide an answer to the biochemist's questions about the chemical details of photosynthesis. Starting with the fact that a plant takes in water and makes sugar and oxygen in the light, one may reasonably ask: Exactly what atomic rearrangements occur? And in what sequence do these atomic rearrangements occur?

The Mechanisms of Chemical Reactions

One of the basic principles of chemical reactions is that only a few atoms are rearranged in any one chemical step. Another is that the number of different molecules coming together in a single chemical reaction almost never exceeds three. Both of these rules are related to the concept of simplicity in chemical reactions. What may seem like a complicated reaction always turns out to be an ordered sequence of simpler reactions. A chemist interested in the "mechanism" of a chemical reaction tries to find out what the simpler component steps are and in what sequence they occur.

41

The formation of sugar in plants is a case in point. The simplest sugars that are found in abundance in plants are glucose and fructose. Each of these compounds has 24 atoms per molecule and can be represented by the molecular formula $C_6H_{12}O_6$. (Note that the *ratio* of carbon to hydrogen to oxygen atoms, 6 to 12 to 6 according to the molecular formula, is the same as that of the empirical formula of sugar, CH_2O.) Glucose and fructose are different compounds because the arrangement of the atoms *within* the molecule is different in the two cases. Since in the last analysis a plant makes all of its compounds as a result of photosynthesis, the six carbon atoms of one molecule of glucose or fructose must come from six different molecules of CO_2. According to the rules of chemical simplicity, six molecules of CO_2 cannot come together at one time in the formation of $C_6H_{12}O_6$. The production of glucose or fructose, therefore, must require a number of individual chemical reactions.

The sequence of reactions involving carbon, starting with CO_2 and ending up with sugar, is called the *pathway of carbon in photosynthesis.* We might design the following experiment to study this sequence. Start with a plant specimen kept in the dark. Then add CO_2 and turn on the light for a short time. Find out by chemical analysis which carbon compound is present that was not present in the dark. Illuminate the plant again, and perform a chemical analysis to find out what the next carbon compound is. Repeat this procedure until the "next carbon compound" identified is the sugar itself.

Unfortunately, such a procedure is possible only in imagination. It cannot be done. The reason is that we cannot deplete a plant of its reserves of these photosynthetic *intermediates* just by placing it in the dark. Turning on the light is not at all like starting up an industrial chemical factory from scratch. Photosynthesis is just one of the processes occurring in the living plant. Hundreds of biochemical reactions are going on at the same time, either making or using some of the same compounds that are important for photosynthesis. All the photosynthetic carbon intermediates are present, at least to some extent, even in a darkened plant.

The Use of Isotopes as Tracers

How, then, can one find out which carbon compounds have just been synthesized by a plant that contains all of the intermediate compounds even before the light is turned on? This could be done easily if there were two kinds of carbon atoms, say (1) and (2). One could use plants that have lived all of their lives with just one type of carbon atom, say (1). This means that all of their photosynthesis has been performed with CO_2 containing only type (1) carbon atoms. Expose such plants to the light in the presence of such CO_2. Then suddenly add to the CO_2 supply some CO_2 containing type (2) carbon atoms. Shortly after adding the new kind of CO_2, kill the plants to stop all biochemical reactions. Then analyze the plant to find out which carbon compounds contain type (2) carbon atoms. These compounds must have been synthesized during the short time of exposure of the plant to the modified-CO_2 supply. If there are only a few such compounds, the obvious conclusion to be drawn is that these are the first organic compounds in the carbon pathway.

Carbon does have several different kinds of atoms, or *isotopes,* as do the other elements. The isotopes of an element have practically identical chemical properties, forming exactly the same compounds with the same formulas. Each isotope of carbon, for example, reacts with oxygen to form CO_2. All molecules of CO_2 that differ only in the carbon isotope they contain have practically identical chemical properties. In any other carbon compound as well, the replacement of one carbon isotope by another results in a compound of practically identical chemical properties.

Needless to say, the isotopes of carbon must differ from each other in some respect other than their chemical properties, or we would not know of their existence. The fundamental difference is that of mass. All atoms of one isotope have the same mass, but atoms of different isotopes have different masses. In fact, it was because of such differences that the existence of isotopes was discovered. Thus, normal carbon, constituting about 99 per cent of all the carbon found on the earth's surface, is called carbon-12, or C^{12}, because its *mass number* is 12. The remaining one per cent of naturally occurring carbon atoms is C^{13} and has a mass number 13. The mass number is almost exactly proportional to the actual weight, or mass, of the atom. Thus, an atom of C^{13} weighs about $13\!/\!12$ as much as an atom of C^{12} (within one part in one thousand).

The difference in mass between different isotopes is *always* observed. A difference that is *sometimes* observed is radioactivity. Neither C^{12} nor C^{13} is radioactive, but a third isotope, C^{14}, is. Carbon-14, which accounts for less than one atom in one million million atoms of natural carbon, can be manufactured readily in a nuclear reactor. Plentiful supplies have been made available as a consequence of developments in nuclear energy. Any radioactive isotope behaves chemically like non-radioactive isotopes of the same element. A radioactive atom, however, is fundamentally unstable, and sooner or later C^{14} will convert spontaneously into an atom of a different chemical element, namely nitrogen. During the process of this conversion, or radioactive decay, a very penetrating high-speed particle is emitted that can be detected by some suitable instrument such as a Geiger counter or a scintillation counter. Although there is no way of predicting when a particular atom will undergo decay, the *average* time that an isotope will survive before it decays is a well-defined property of that isotope. The *average lifetime* of C^{14}, for example, is slightly more than 8000 years. The average lifetime of a radioactive isotope should not be confused with the related property of *half-life*, the period in which one-half of the atoms present in a sample will disintegrate radioactively. The rate at which a radioactive isotope decays is usually described in terms of its half-life. The half-life of C^{14} is 5700 years.

Radioactive isotopes are useful because they can be detected so easily. Thus C^{14} is a very good tool for studying the complex carbon chemistry of photosynthesis. In practice, a suspension of algae or a leaf is allowed to photosynthesize in normal CO_2. At some point, CO_2 containing C^{14} atoms is added to the atmosphere of the sample. Shortly afterwards, the leaf or the algae sample is killed by quickly immersing it in boiling water or alcohol. The compounds of the plants are extracted from the dead cells and separated by standard chemical procedures. Of the hundreds of known plant compounds, only a few are found to contain C^{14} atoms. Since the only source of C^{14} was the newly added CO_2, these few compounds must have been formed as the first products of CO_2-absorption in photosynthesis. The C^{14} is said to be a *tracer*, because it allows the experimenter to distinguish a newly formed molecule of a substance (containing C^{14}) from all the other molecules of the same substance (containing C^{12} or C^{13}) that were already there prior to the experiment.

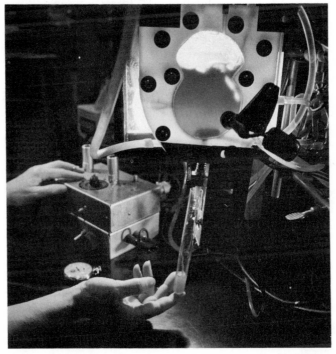

Jon Brenneis

Fig. 5-1. "Lollypop" apparatus used by Melvin Calvin's group. An algae sample is removed by pressing a button on the sampler control. Alcohol in the test tube kills the algae.

The Carbon Intermediates of Photosynthesis

The first comprehensive set of experiments employing C^{14} were begun shortly after World War II by Melvin Calvin, J. A. Bassham, Andrew A. Benson and their associates at the University of California. The kind of apparatus used is illustrated in Figure 5–1. The principal experiments were performed with suspensions of *Chlorella* or another green alga, *Scenedesmus*. They found that if they waited as long as 30 seconds after adding the radioactive CO_2 before killing the cells, the radioactivity was already distributed in a dozen or more compounds. But by progressively shortening the exposure time to only two seconds, they found almost all the C^{14} incorporated in just one compound (see Fig. 5–2). Therefore, this one compound must be the first chemically *stable* product of CO_2-absorption in the photosynthetic carbon cycle. (An unstable product might have decomposed during the operation of immersing the algae in boiling alcohol or water.) This key compound, *phosphoglyceric acid*, or PGA, is a well-known compound occurring in practically all animal and plant cells. PGA can be thought of as having two important parts, one mineral and the other organic. Actually PGA can be split easily into these components by a simple chemical procedure. The mineral component is phosphoric acid, a common inorganic chemical; the organic part is glyceric acid, which has the molecular formula $C_3H_6O_4$. The technical term for this type of combination of an organic molecule with phosphoric acid is *phosphate ester*.

From experiments done with longer and longer exposures to radioactive CO_2 in the light, Calvin and his group were able to describe a sequence of more than a dozen reactions involved in the photosynthetic carbon cycle. Their work has subsequently been confirmed and extended by other investigators. PGA seems to play a key role not only in green algae, but also in the other algae, in leaves, and even in photosynthetic bacteria. The other stable compounds found along the carbon pathway between CO_2 and the six-carbon sugars (glucose and fructose) are either sugars or the phosphate

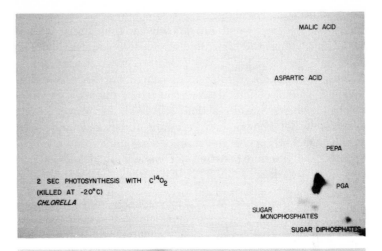

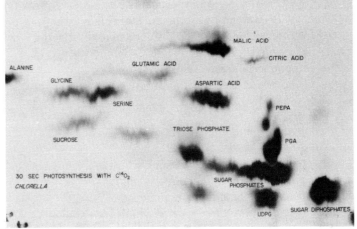

Lawrence Radiation Laboratory

Fig. 5-2. The carbon intermediates of photosynthesis in these chromatograms were separated by paper chromatography: One solvent carried compounds up the sheet (from a drop of algae extract in bottom right corner); a second solvent, across the sheet. Sheets were stored in contact with X-ray film. Compounds containing radioactive carbon, (introduced in $C^{14}O_2$) exposed the film, producing dark spots when it was developed. Compounds were identified by comparing spots with chromatograms of known compounds. After two seconds of photosynthesis (top), PGA contains almost all the C^{14}; after 30 seconds (bottom), many compounds contain C^{14}.

esters of sugars. These sugars contain 3, 4, 5, 6, or 7 carbon atoms per molecule and are known by the generic names *triose, tetrose, pentose, hexose,* and *heptose* respectively. The phosphate esters of the trioses (3-carbon sugars) are the first of these to be made in the photosynthetic sequence.

Which, if any, of the dozen or so reactions involving carbon is a true photochemical reaction? Although the answer to this question is not known with certainty, it has definitely been established that some of the reactions are dark reactions. Specifically, the reaction in which CO_2 is absorbed and PGA is formed is a dark reaction. This was proved by the following experimental procedure. The algae were allowed to photosynthesize in the light with normal CO_2; the light was turned off and radioactive CO_2 was added. When the algae were killed and analyzed, C^{14} was found in the PGA. The PGA did not acquire C^{14} in separate experiments performed entirely in the dark. The inference was drawn that while light was required for the production of a substance that absorbs the CO_2, it was not needed for the absorption reaction itself.

The compounds immediately following PGA in the carbon pathway, the trioses, seem to be produced less abundantly in the dark than they are in the light. Evidence for this is the fact that the total amount of PGA in the algae is greater in the dark than in the light. The conclusion has been drawn that either the trioses are made directly from PGA in the light, or they are made in the dark by an almost instantaneous reaction of PGA with a substance made in the light.

The first stable compound containing newly acquired carbon atoms, PGA, contains three carbon atoms. A detailed experiment with radioactive CO_2 has shown that only one of the three carbon atoms in the newly formed PGA is radioactive. PGA might therefore be formed from the reaction of one CO_2 molecule with some two-carbon compound (containing nonradioactive carbon atoms) already present in the plant at the time of addition of the radioactive CO_2. No two-carbon compound which reacts in the dark with CO_2 to give PGA has been identified in green plants. Instead, experimenters have found a five-carbon sugar (or pentose) whose concentration always appeared to decrease when the concentration of PGA increased, and *vice versa*. This particular pentose occurs in a phosphate ester known as ribulose diphosphate, or RDP. In the light, the concentration of RDP in algae is very low in the presence of CO_2 and relatively higher in the absence of CO_2. In the dark, the concentration of RDP is lower than in the light. Conversely, the concentration of PGA is greater in the dark than in the light, and is lower in the absence of CO_2 than in its presence. All these facts point to the conclusion that RDP is the substance that accepts CO_2 to form PGA. This reaction has since been discovered to occur even outside the living cell.

The further details of the carbon pathway are summarized in the following list of reactions:

a. $RDP(5) + CO_2(1) + ? \rightsquigarrow PGA(3) + Triose(3) + ?$

b. $RDP(5) + CO_2(1) \longrightarrow PGA(3) + PGA(3)$

c. $PGA(3) + ? \rightsquigarrow Triose(3) + ?$

d. $Triose(3) + Triose(3) \longrightarrow Hexose(6)$

e. $Hexose(6) + Triose(3) \longrightarrow Pentose(5) + Tetrose(4)$

f. $Tetrose(4) + Triose(3) \longrightarrow Heptose(7)$

g. $Heptose(7) + Triose(3) \longrightarrow Pentose(5) + Pentose(5)$

h. $Pentose(5) \rightsquigarrow RDP(5)$

The numbers in parentheses give the number of carbon atoms per molecule. For purposes of simplification, phosphoric acid is not included and the state of combination of the various substances with phosphoric acid is not indicated except for PGA and RDP. All reactions that have straight arrows ($\longrightarrow$) are reactions in which no chemical energy is stored. All of them occur in the dark. The three reactions marked with wavy arrows ($\rightsquigarrow$) are energy-storing reactions that require either the direct use of light energy or the use of energy-rich chemicals made in the light. If the energy-rich chemicals are not taken up quickly in these reactions, they disappear by "side" reactions not connected with the photosynthetic cycle. Thus, reactions *a*, *c*, and *h* do not occur readily in the dark. Reactions *a* and *b* are alternate pathways for the reaction of

RDP with CO_2. The relative importance of these two reactions is still not known with certainty.

The reaction table helps to explain certain experimental facts. When the light is turned off, only the non-photochemical reactions can proceed. RDP is converted to PGA by reaction b ($\longrightarrow$), but PGA cannot be removed by reaction c ($\leadsto$); nor can RDP be replaced by reaction h ($\leadsto$). Thus, the concentration of RDP decreases in the dark, while the concentration of PGA increases.

The Cyclic Nature of the Reaction Scheme

The set of reactions listed above constitutes a cycle. Every reactant appearing on the left-hand side (except CO_2) also appears as a product on the right-hand side. In particular, RDP, the compound that accepts CO_2, is itself a product of photosynthesis. The progress of photosynthesis under steady illumination requires that RDP and all of the other intermediate carbon compounds be present at their proper concentrations so that the different steps can be properly synchronized. Even under optimum conditions, photosynthesis does not start at its maximum rate when the light is turned on after a dark period of several minutes; rather, it gradually builds up from zero to its steady high rate over the course of a minute or so. This interval is the *induction period* required for all of the intermediate compounds to reach their proper concentrations. The induction period is especially long in the case of RDP, because the concentration of RDP falls practically to zero in the dark. When the light is first turned on, the initial photosynthetic activity produces only very small amounts of RDP. As the RDP concentration gradually increases, the rate of photosynthesis increases to its final steady value.

How is the storage of chemical energy possible if all of the products are re-used in the cycle of keeping the "machinery" going? The answer is that not all of the products *are* re-cycled. Some of the hexose made in reaction d is stored as a final product, and only part of it is used in reaction e to replenish the RDP used in the first step. Careful bookkeeping shows

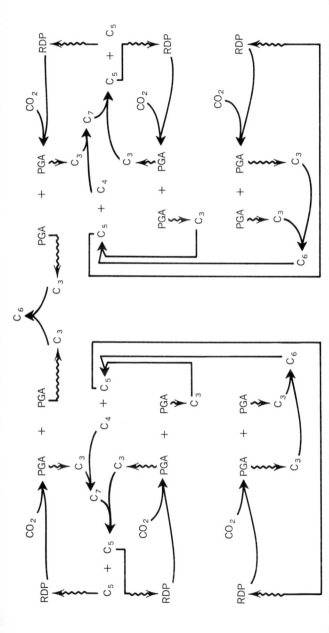

Fig. 5-3. The carbon cycle of photosynthesis. This diagram summarizes all the reactions from **b** through **h** discussed in the text. Note that for every six carbon-dioxide molecules that enter the cycle, one hexose molecule (C_6) leaves it as a final product. All the other carbon compounds are intermediates; they are reused as often as they are formed in photosynthesis. The wavy arrows represent steps that require energy. The draining off of intermediates for the synthesis of fats and proteins is not shown. For the sake of simplicity, this scheme omits reaction **a**, which is a possible natural alternative for the combined reactions **b** and **c**.

that one hexose molecule is drawn off as the net product for every six molecules of CO_2 absorbed, even if the other sugars —the trioses, tetroses, pentoses, and heptoses, are completely re-cycled (see Fig. 5–3). The overall balance of *carbon* atoms would then follow the equation:

$$6 \text{ RDP}(5) + 6 \text{ CO}_2(1) \longrightarrow \text{Hexose}(6) + 6 \text{ RDP}(5)$$

The hexose molecules taken from the photosynthetic cycle may be used partly to store energy that the plant can later draw on for its general needs. Some of the hexoses may react non-photochemically to form other compounds, such as sucrose (common table sugar) or starch, the major storage product in many of the higher plants. Fats, proteins, and other classes of organic compounds may also be synthesized by the plants from starting materials drawn from different stages of the carbon cycle.

Most of the reactions of the carbon cycle are self-contained in that the only additional compounds involved are the common mineral substances water and phosphoric acid. Reactions *a* and *c* are exceptions, in that other compounds are involved.

a. $\text{RDP}(5) + \text{CO}_2(1) + ? \rightsquigarrow \text{PGA}(3) + \text{Triose}(3) + ?$

c. $\text{PGA}(3) + ? \rightsquigarrow \text{Triose}(3) + ?$

These other substances, represented by question marks, link the photosynthetic carbon cycle to the production of oxygen. The nature of the connection between the carbon intermediates and the evolution of oxygen will be discussed in the next chapter.

6

The Pathway of Oxygen and a More General View of Photosynthesis

Experiments with Oxygen Isotopes

The use of isotopic tracers is not nearly so successful in following the pathway of oxygen as of carbon. Although radioactive isotopes of oxygen can be made, they are almost useless for experiments in photosynthesis. The atoms are so unstable that their average lifetime before undergoing radioactive decay is less than four minutes. This is not long enough to carry out a complete experiment easily. There is a stable isotope, however, that can be used. This is O^{18}, which constitutes only 0.2 per cent of all oxygen atoms in the atmosphere and oceans. Oxygen-18 can be separated from the common isotope, O^{16}, by special procedures. Both water and CO_2 can be prepared containing a very high percentage of O^{18}. Used as a tracer in chemical experiments, the heavier isotope can be distinguished from O^{16} by means of a *mass spectrometer*, which separates individual molecules according to their mass.

Is it CO_2 or water that furnishes the oxygen atoms for the oxygen gas produced in photosynthesis? In 1941, Samuel Ruben and M. D. Kamen performed two experiments to answer this question. In one experiment, a suspension of algae was made up in water containing excess O^{18}, and "normal" CO_2 was introduced. In the second, CO_2 containing excess O^{18} was bubbled through a suspension containing ordinary water. In both experiments, the lights were turned on and the oxygen produced by photosynthesis was collected. This oxygen gas was placed in a mass spectrometer to see whether it contained the normal isotopic content or the excess O^{18}. The results showed that when the water contained excess O^{18} and the CO_2 was normal, the evolved oxygen contained the same excess of O^{18} as the water. Similarly, when these conditions were reversed, the evolved oxygen was found to have the normal isotopic composition. Obviously, the atoms that made up the oxygen gas must have come from the water.

This result may appear to contradict the overall equation of photosynthesis,

$$CO_2 + H_2O \longrightarrow O_2 + \{CH_2O\}$$

which shows water supplying only *one* oxygen atom, whereas the tracer experiment shows *both* atoms of oxygen coming from water. The paradox is not real, however. A chemical equation such as this one is simply a balance sheet for the whole reaction, showing what is used up and what is produced. More than one molecule of water may participate in the reaction, so long as the net consumption of water is one molecule. For example, if two molecules of water were reactants (to the left of the arrow) and one molecule of water appeared as a product (on the right), the net consumption would still be one molecule and we could see that both atoms of O_2 might come from water.

Photosynthesis is often described as the *splitting of water*. This is not a precise scientific definition; it merely points out that the oxygen from water ends up in one of the products, oxygen gas, while the hydrogen ends up in another, the sugar. (The hydrogen atoms of the sugar must, of course, come from water, because water is the only reactant containing hydrogen.) The actual processes by which water is split are very complicated and include a large number of chemical steps.

The experimental procedures for studying the pathway of oxygen are in principle the same as those used to determine the pathway of carbon. What is the first compound, other than water, to incorporate O^{18} atoms when algae are first illuminated in water containing O^{18}? Curiously enough, the answer is oxygen gas itself. Apparently, any intermediate compounds containing oxygen are present only in extremely small amounts or are so unstable that they decompose during the extraction process before they can be analyzed. Most scientists believe that some oxygen-containing intermediate compounds must be formed at one stage of photosynthesis and decomposed into oxygen gas in later stages. This view is based on the general principle of chemical simplicity mentioned in Chapter 5. Unfortunately, such intermediate compounds may be too unstable to be identified by standard chemical procedures.

Difference Spectroscopy

Unstable intermediate compounds can be identified by analytical procedures carried out on the living plant itself. If a measurement is made during or very shortly after a period of photosynthesis, then even an unstable intermediate can be detected before it decomposes.

One ingenious method that has been used is *difference spectroscopy*, which is based on the well-known fact that every chemical substance absorbs light of only certain wavelengths. For each substance, the set of wavelengths absorbed, together with the percentage absorption at each of these wavelengths, constitutes the *absorption spectrum* of that substance. (Examples will be given in Chapter 7.) The amount of light absorbed can easily be measured without disturbing the living cell. A beam of light is passed through a sample and the percentage of the light absorbed is measured by a light detector. The principle is illustrated in Figure 6–1.

The absorption spectrum of a single plant cell is a composite of the absorption spectra of the hundreds of compounds that make up the cell, but it gives no information about the sequence in which various compounds are produced. A more valuable measurement would be the *difference* in the percentage absorption by an algae sample following a period of illumination and following a period of darkness. Any difference would result from chemical changes induced by photosynthesis. In particular, unstable photosynthetic intermediates formed in the light but not surviving in the dark, contribute to such a *difference* spectrum. Measurements of this type, performed since 1950 in a number of laboratories, have shown several such intermediates.

Once a certain compound is known to be formed in the light, we next want to know where this formation occurs in the photosynthetic sequence. L. N. M. Duysens of the University of Leiden attempted to trace the sequence of chemical events leading to oxygen production by the following experiment. He added a synthetic plant poison, DCMU, to his algae suspension. This weed killer is known to interfere with photosynthesis by preventing a particular reaction connected with oxygen production, for an amount of DCMU sufficient to stop photosynthesis in green algae has no effect on the rate of photoreduction, in which no oxygen is evolved. Duysens reasoned that if one of the intermediate steps in the production of oxygen is blocked by DCMU, all products of the preceding

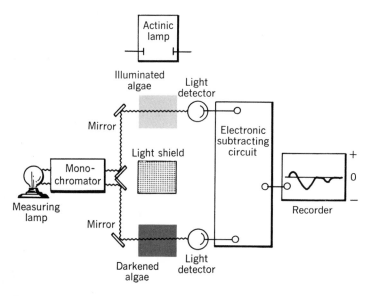

Fig. 6-1. Difference spectrometer. The "measuring light" is split into two beams and directed into separate algae suspensions by means of mirrors. The upper suspension photosynthesizes under the influence of the actinic lamp; the lower suspension, kept in the dark, does not (the effect of the weak measuring beam is negligible). Each light detector generates a signal proportional to the beam intensity, and the difference is recorded. As the wavelength of the light changes, the recorder traces out a difference spectrum.

steps would pile up like cars on a crowded highway. He performed the experiment with a suspension of poisoned algae and found, by difference spectroscopy, that a substance known as cytochrome f is changed in the light from its normal form, called the "reduced form," to the "oxidized form." Duysens repeated the experiment with unpoisoned algae and did not observe any change in cytochrome f. He concluded that the oxidized form of cytochrome f is made in the chain of events leading to oxygen evolution. The oxidized form could not be detected without poisoning the algae because it is a short-lived intermediate in normal photosynthesis, being made in one step and changed back to its reduced form almost immediately by a following step.

Is cytochrome f on the oxygen pathway in photosynthesis? The chemistry of this substance makes it difficult to give a straightforward answer to this question. Cytochrome f, a colored material found in plants, belongs to a class of *enzymes* (proteins having the ability to speed up specific biological reactions) known in both plants and animals. All of these cytochromes occur in two forms, reduced and oxidized. Their molecules are large, containing hundreds of atoms, with very slight differences in chemical content between the two forms. This difference is not a difference in the number of oxygen atoms per molecule. Although the conversion of reduced to oxidized cytochrome f may be an essential link in the chain leading to oxygen evolution, the role of cytochrome does not appear to be that of passing an oxygen atom along this chain. To explain this apparent paradox, we must now digress from our story of photosynthesis to examine the relationship between oxidized and reduced forms of chemical substances in general.

The Chemistry of Oxidation-Reduction Reactions

The terms *oxidized* and *reduced* were first applied to metals more than 100 years ago. When a bar of iron rusts in air, to take a familiar example, the iron is said to be oxidized. The oxygen of the air needed for the reaction is called the *oxidizing agent.* Rust contains iron atoms, but the iron atoms are not in the same state as in metallic iron. The oxidized state of the iron in rust is the same as in certain iron ores, including rouge. To restore the iron atoms to their metallic state it is necessary to heat the rust or iron ore with certain substances that reverse the effect of the oxidation. Examples of such substances are aluminum and carbon monoxide. The restoration process is called *reduction,* and the aluminum or carbon monoxide is the *reducing agent.* The metallic state of iron is therefore the *reduced state.*

We know today that oxidation is a much more common process than the reaction with oxygen. Iron atoms can be brought to the same oxidized condition by reaction with a wide variety of oxidizing agents, chlorine gas, some saltlike compounds of the element cerium, and some oxides of lead and manganese, to name just a few. What the oxidizing agent does in each case is to remove three electrons from an iron atom. (An iron atom in its reduced, or metallic, state, has a total of 26 electrons.)

In Chapter 2 we discussed the photoelectric effect, another process for removing electrons from metals. There is a basic difference between the photoelectric and the chemical removal of electrons. In a photoelectric experiment, the illuminated metal surface ejects electrons but regains them by the flow of electrons through the wires used to complete the electrical circuit. Thus a permanent loss of electrons, or oxidation of the metal, does not occur. In the chemical event, however, there is a permanent transfer of electrons from the metal to the oxidizing agent. Not only does the metal become permanently oxidized, but a permanent change also takes place in the oxidizing agent—the electrons lost by the metal are captured by the oxidizing agent. Thus the oxidizing agent also exists in two forms, with and without the additional electrons. By analogy with the metal, we can call the form containing the larger number of electrons the reduced form, and the form with the smaller number of electrons the oxidized form.

In other words, oxidation and reduction must occur simultaneously. In a chemical reaction, when one substance is oxidized (loses electrons), another substance is reduced (gains electrons). A substance and the oxidized form of that substance together constitute what chemists refer to as a *couple*. Similarly, a substance and the reduced form following reduction also constitute a couple. Any oxidation-reduction reaction may be written as:

oxidized form of couple 1 + reduced form of couple 2 $\longrightarrow$
reduced form of couple 1 + oxidized form of couple 2.

This reaction may also be described verbally by saying that couple 1 oxidizes couple 2. If this reaction occurs readily, then the reverse reaction does not; that is, couple 2 would not oxidize couple 1.

In fact, there is a whole hierarchy of couples. They may be listed in a particular order such that any couple on the list can oxidize any couple *below* it, but not any couple *above* it. In such a list, the couples are ordered on the basis of their *standard electrode potential*, or S.E.P. (The term *electrode* is used because one way of measuring this quantity is by an electrical measurement involving the insertion of wire electrodes into a solution containing both members of the couple.) The couples with the largest values of the S.E.P. (at the top of the list) contain the best oxidizing agents, and those with the smallest values (at the bottom) contain the poorest oxidizing agents. The scale normally used has both *positive* and *negative* values. The sign of a single couple's S.E.P. is not as important as whether its S.E.P. is *algebraically* larger or smaller than another.

The S.E.P. values for several couples are listed in Table 6–1. In most cases, special names are not given to the reduced and oxidized forms. Values for the S.E.P.'s would change with variations in temperature and acidity from the average conditions in living plants cells. The S.E.P. values in Table 6–1 are those obtained with neutral solutions (neither acidic nor basic) at a temperature of 25°C.

The rule that a couple will oxidize any couple of a lower S.E.P. is a simplification. It applies strictly only if the concentrations of the chemicals forming the two couples are the same.

If the difference in S.E.P.'s is great, then the rule is applicable even for large concentration differences, and the predicted reaction may go to completion. If the difference in S.E.P.'s is small, the reaction may go one way or the other, depending on the relative concentrations. If the concentrations are all the same for a small difference in S.E.P.'s, the reaction will proceed in the predicted direction, but only to a limited extent.

Table 6–1. Some standard electrode potentials of couples.

Couple	Oxidized Form	Reduced Form	S.E.P. (volts)
Gold			1.50
Y			?
	Oxygen gas	Water	0.82
Silver			0.80
Cytochrome f			0.36
Copper			0.34
NADP			−0.32
	PGA-phosphate	Triose + phosphoric acid	−0.35
	Water	Hydrogen Gas	−0.41
	CO_2	Glucose	−0.43
Ferredoxin			−0.43
X			?
Sodium			−2.71

We can now illustrate the use of the table with some examples. Oxygen (S.E.P. = 0.82) can readily tarnish (oxidize) copper (S.E.P. = 0.34), can just barely begin to tarnish silver (S.E.P. = 0.80), and cannot tarnish gold (S.E.P. = 1.50) at all. Sodium metal (S.E.P. = −2.71) is oxidized by water (S.E.P. = −0.41) even in the absence of oxygen gas, because −0.41 is algebraically greater than −2.71.

The S.E.P. value of a couple is related to the difference in chemical energy between the oxidized and reduced forms of that couple. We can simply take it as a fact that one chemical is a better oxidizing agent (remover of electrons) than another. The listing of substances in the order of their ability to react may be understood by drawing an analogy with a military hierarchy. Consider every individual in a military organization as having just two kinds of functions, to give orders to his subordinates and to carry out the orders of his superiors. A captain may give orders to a lieutenant, sergeant, or private, but not to a major, colonel, or general. Conversely, the captain must obey orders of a major, colonel, or general, but does not take orders from a lieutenant, sergeant, or private. Similarly, each oxidation-reduction couple has two kinds of functions. In the first case, the oxidized member acts as an oxidizing agent with respect to another couple; in the second, the reduced member is oxidized by another couple. Thus, the oxidized form of copper may oxidize hydrogen gas or sodium metal but not silver or gold. On the other hand, copper metal is oxidized by the oxidized forms of silver and gold, but not by water or the oxidized form of sodium.

Photosynthesis as Oxidation-Reduction

We can now apply these ideas to photosynthesis. The chemical job of green plants is to make sugars and oxygen gas. This can be described as the oxidation of water to oxygen and the simultaneous reduction of CO_2 to sugar. From the rules of oxidation-reduction, CO_2 should not be able to oxidize water by itself. On the S.E.P. scale, the CO_2-glucose couple (-0.43 volt) is well below the water-oxygen couple ($+0.82$ volt). The voltage difference that must be overcome (1.25 volts) is proportional to the amount of chemical energy stored by photosynthesis, and it is only by the conversion of light energy that the process can proceed.

Actually, we know that the true photochemical reactions of photosynthesis produce neither glucose nor oxygen. These final products are formed in dark reactions that must obey the normal rules of oxidation-reduction. The role of the light reactions is to make an oxidizing agent powerful enough to oxidize water spontaneously to oxygen gas and to make a reducing agent powerful enough to reduce CO_2. Even without knowing what these photochemical products are, we can say something about their properties. If the couple that produces oxygen is designated as Y, the S.E.P. of Y must be close to or greater than 0.82 volt (the value for water-oxygen). If the couple

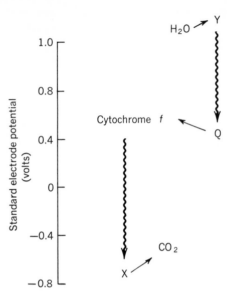

Fig. 6-2. Electron flow in photosynthesis. Arrows represent transfer of electrons from reducing to oxidizing agent; electrons must be transferred from a couple of lower S.E.P. to one of higher S.E.P. Thus, only upward-pointing arrows correspond to natural dark processes; downward pointing arrows, to processes requiring light energy. **X** is a strong reducing agent, made in the light, that can reduce carbon compounds in the dark; **Y** is a strong oxidizing agent, also made in the light, that can oxidize water to oxygen gas in the dark. **Q** is a possible intermediate connecting these two light reactions.

that will reduce CO_2 is X, then the S.E.P. of X must be about −0.43 (the value for CO_2-glucose) or less. (See Fig. 6–2.)

As for X, its participation in the carbon pathway must be by way of an oxidation-reduction reaction. Of all the participating carbon reactions listed in Chapter 5 (page 49), only two are of the oxidation-reduction type. These two are *a* and *c*, the reactions in which the first sugar, triose, is made:

a. $RDP + CO_2 + ? \longrightarrow PGA + Triose + ?$

c. $PGA + ? \longrightarrow Triose + ?$

Two possibilities exist for the role of X. Either X is the carbon compound (PGA or the RDP-CO_2 combination) that is reduced in the light to triose, or it is a different substance reduced in the light and capable of forming triose in the dark by reaction *a* or *c*. In the second case, X plays the role of the question mark in these reactions, appearing on the left of the arrow in its reduced form and on the right in its oxidized form. In this case, reaction *a* or reaction *c* might be complex, consisting of several successive steps. Ferredoxin, a substance known generally to occur in plants, has been included in the table to show that it meets some of the requirements demanded of X. NADP (formerly known as TPN) is an enzyme that is capable of promoting oxidation-reduction reactions involving PGA, and has been suggested as an intermediate in reactions *a* and *c*. Most of our information on the role of these substances come from experiments on plant-cell extracts, to be discussed in Chapter 9.

The significance of cytochrome *f* in photosynthesis can now be discussed. The difference in S.E.P. for the overall photosynthetic process, 1.25 volts, does not have to be overcome all in one photochemical step. If cytochrome *f* were oxidized in the same photochemical step that reduces X, the potential difference for this step would be about 0.79 volt (0.36 for cytochrome *f* *minus* −0.43 for X). The second stage of energy storage would involve either the direct or indirect reaction of cytochrome *f* with Y to give the oxidized form of Y. This stage would involve a minimum potential difference of 0.46 volt (0.82 for Y *minus* 0.36). The break-down of the energy-storage steps of photosynthesis could then be represented as follows:

(1)   X(oxidized) + cytochrome *f*(reduced) ⤳
        X(reduced) + cytochrome *f*(oxidized)

(2)   Y(reduced) + cytochrome *f*(oxidized) ⤳
        Y(oxidized) + cytochrome *f*(reduced)

Apparently, something like this occurs in green plants, where the energy of two quanta are needed to overcome the total S.E.P. difference. If the two quanta act on different reactions, there is no violation of Einstein's Law of Photochemistry. In Chapter 2 it was pointed out that eight quanta are needed for the amount of photosynthesis represented by the equation

$$CO_2 + H_2O \longrightarrow O_2 + \{CH_2O\}$$

Each molecule of CO_2 that is reduced requires four molecules of reduced X (one quantum each), and each oxygen molecule produced requires four molecules of oxidized Y (one quantum each). This adds up to the total quantum requirement of eight.

Thus cytochrome f is on the way toward overcoming the total S.E.P. difference of photosynthesis. In this sense it is on the pathway of oxygen evolution, even though it may not contain oxygen atoms that will ultimately appear in the oxygen gas. Clearly, much still needs to be learned about the pathway of oxygen evolution—the identification of Y; the identification of the steps, if any, between reactions (1) and (2); and the process by which four molecules of oxidized Y react with water to restore reduced Y and produce one molecule of O_2.

7

The Plant Pigments

One basic law of photochemistry is that light must be absorbed in order to be effective. Particularly, light in the visible spectrum must be absorbed by some substance or substances in the plant in order to initiate the photochemical reactions of photosynthesis. Both CO_2 and water, however, are transparent to visible light; that is, they do not absorb light. The light needed for photosynthesis must, therefore, be absorbed by substances that do not themselves undergo a net change in the process. This chapter deals with the properties of these plant pigments as pure chemicals, and the next chapter will discuss the distinctive properties of the pigments in the living cell.

Extraction and Identification of Plant Pigments

Chlorophyll is the principal photosynthetic pigment of plants. This is the substance that gives green plants their characteristic color. It accounts for as much as five per cent of the total dry weight of some algae. Although it is insoluble in water, chlorophyll can be extracted from the green tissue of plants with such organic solvents as acetone or ether. Such extracts were the only source of pure chlorophyll until 1960, when this pigment was synthesized for the first time by Robert Woodward of Harvard University.

A plant extract that contains chlorophyll contains other substances as well, many of which are deeply colored. One of the best ways of separating these various pigments is the technique of *chromatography*, invented in 1906 by the Russian botanist Mikhail Tswett. In this method, illustrated in Figure 7-1, a glass tube is packed with a suitable, colorless powdered

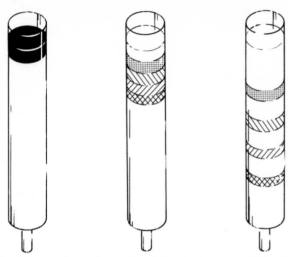

Fig. 7-1. Column chromatography. A band of unseparated pigments (left) is separated into single-pigment bands by pouring a suitable solvent in at the top of the column (center and right).

substance such as sugar or chalk, called the *adsorbent,* and a concentrated extract of pigments is then poured in at the top of the column. The pigments appear as a colored band at the top of the column, as shown on the left in Figure 7–1. A pure solvent, called the *developer,* is then added slowly at the top and allowed to flow through the column, eventually coming out at the bottom. As the developer flows through, the pigments move slowly downward, and the original band of mixed pigments separates into several bands (center and right in Figure 7–1). This stage of the procedure is called *development.* The different bands have different colors because, in theory at least, each band contains just one pigment. The various bands move down the column at different rates, the lowest band moving the most rapidly. The development procedure may be stopped at any point after the bands are well enough separated, by stopping the flow of developer at the top. The whole column of adsorbent can then be pushed out of the top of the tube without disturbing the stratification of the bands. Once it has been removed from the glass tube, the adsorbent column is sliced into separate bands. When a single band is treated with fresh solvent, the pigment dissolves and a clear solution of that one pigment component is obtained.

The principle of this method is fairly simple. When a solvent is poured into the column a "competition" for pigment molecules begins between the liquid solvent and the solid adsorbent. This is based on the difference between the solvent and the adsorbent in their chemical forces of attraction for the pigment. The attractive forces of the adsorbent must not be very great, because excess developer will always take the pigment from the adsorbent and carry it further down the tube. The important point is that the attraction of the adsorbent, weak though it may be, is different for the various pigments. It is the *difference* in the attractive forces that makes the separation possible.

Although the chromatographic method may be applied even to colorless substances, it is especially easy to use when we can see the color of the various banded components. It is not surprising that Tswett first applied his method to the problem of separating the pigments of green-leaf extracts. His experiments proved that a typical leaf contains two different green pigments and several yellow or orange pigments.

Chlorophylls

The two green pigments are now called chlorophyll *a* and chlorophyll *b;* the first is a bluish green and the second a yellowish green. Chlorophyll *a* is the one pigment common to all green plants. It is present even in algae that do not look green, the red and brown algae, for example. Chlorophyll *b* is present in all leaves and in the green algae, but not in the red, brown, and blue-green algae. Several other pigments of the chlorophyll family are known, the most important of which, bacteriochlorophyll, occurs in the photosynthetic bacteria. These bacteria, unlike the green plants that carry out normal photosynthesis, do not contain any chlorophyll *a*.

The chlorophylls are all related chemically. They are complex molecules containing magnesium, oxygen, nitrogen, carbon, and hydrogen. Each molecule contains over 100 atoms, and the differences in atomic composition of the various chlorophylls are relatively small. This class of compounds is related to the *hemes*, another important group of biochemicals, which contain iron instead of magnesium. The hemes occur, for example, in the hemoglobin of the blood and in the cytochrome enzymes of plants and animals.

The different chlorophylls can be distinguished by their absorption spectra. Figure 7–2 shows the absorption spectra for solutions of chlorophylls *a* and *b* and of bacteriochlorophyll dissolved in ether. Note that both *a* and *b* absorb a good deal of light at the blue (4000 to 4600Å) and red (6300 to 6800Å) ends of the visible spectrum. Their green appearance corresponds to the very weak absorption (and thus high transmission) of green light (5000 to 5500Å). A distinctive feature of bacteriochlorophyll is the very strong absorption in the infrared region between 7500 and 8000Å.

Other Pigments

The yellow and orange pigments separated from leaf extracts belong to a class known as the *carotenoids*. There is a large number of these pigments, and there is considerable variety in their occurrence in different plants. Their total amount is usually less than that of chlorophyll. The yellow and orange colors of fall leaves are due partly to carotenoids, which do not deteriorate so rapidly as the chlorophylls with the approach of the winter season.

Another class of pigments are the *phycobilins*, or *biliproteins*, found in red and blue-green algae. Their concentration in these algae may be several times greater than that of chlorophyll. These pigments, as opposed to the chlorophylls and carotenoids, are water-soluble. There are two main members of this class, the red *phycoerythrin* and the blue *phycocyanin*. These pigments strongly absorb colors which chlorophyll does not, namely, green and orange respectively.

All three classes of pigments described above are involved in photosynthesis. All of them absorb appreciable amounts of

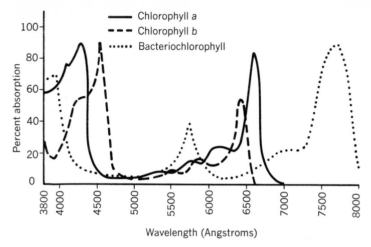

Fig. 7-2. Absorption spectra of chlorophyll extracts dissolved in ether. The curves have been adjusted to make the maximum absorption within the visible spectrum 90 percent for each solution.

light that can be used, to some extent at least, for photosynthetic energy conversion.

Fluorescence

Some light absorbers, including chlorophyll and the phycobilins, have the ability to emit light while being irradiated. Such compounds are said to be *fluorescent*. The wavelengths of a fluorescence spectrum, which is characteristic of the substance in question, are always longer than the wavelengths of the corresponding absorption spectrum, and are usually concentrated in one region. Chlorophyll-*a* extracts, for example, absorb strongly in the blue and the red regions of the spectrum, but fluoresce only in the red. The maximum intensity of chlorophyll-*a* fluorescence occurs at 6680Å, compared to the wavelengths of maximum absorption at 4300Å and 6620Å. For chlorophyll-*b*, the fluorescence peak is at 6480Å and the absorption peaks are at 4530Å and 6425Å. This shift to longer wavelengths makes it very easy to observe fluorescence. By illuminating with a short-wavelength light, one can induce fluorescence of a different color at a longer wavelength. This can be demonstrated easily with any healthy green leaf that is not dried out. All one has to do is cover a lamp with a blue filter—a piece of blue glass or transparent blue paper will do—and, in an otherwise darkened room, illuminate the leaf with the blue light. You will see the red fluorescence coming from the leaf in all directions. An acetone extract of a leaf will fluoresce even more strongly.

The study of fluorescence tells us a great deal about how a pigment is used in photochemistry. The light emitted in fluorescence is, of course, a form of energy. The fluorescence of molecules, however, does not account for all the light energy absorbed by the molecule. The experimental evidence for this conclusion is that the fluorescence spectrum is shifted toward longer wavelengths compared with the absorption spectrum. And we have already seen that the energy of a quantum of light decreases with increasing wavelength. If, as is the case with photosynthetic pigments, the pigment molecule does not undergo any permanent change, some type of energy loss other than fluorescence must occur in order to account for the difference. Usually, the energy that is not emitted by fluorescence is dissipated in the form of heat when photochemical reactions do not take place.

The various processes by which a pigment molecule loses absorbed energy are shown in Figure 7–3. The molecule, even without undergoing any chemical change, can "occupy" a number of different *energy states*. Each horizontal line represents a single energy state of the molecule, and the height of the line is proportional to the energy of that state. The lowest of these, the *ground state* (A in Figure 7–3), is the state in which the molecule is normally found. When the molecule absorbs light, the light energy is converted into internal energy of the molecule. This process is called *excitation*, and the molecule is said to exist in an *excited* (higher energy) *state*. The excess energy of an excited state is related to the internal motions of the atoms and to changes in the positions occupied by the electrons within the molecule. Actually there are many possible excited states within a molecule. The particular state resulting

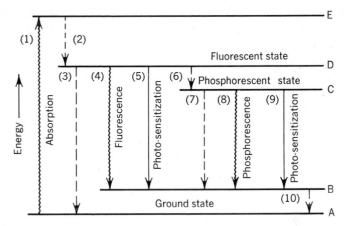

Fig. 7-3. Some energy processes involving pigment molecules. Vertical distances are proportional to the energy. Light processes are represented by wavy arrows; dissipation of heat energy, by dashed arrows; photochemical processes, by solid arrows.

from the absorption of light depends on the wavelength of light. There is a general rule that the energy contained in the light quantum must exactly equal the difference in energy between the ground state and the particular excited state produced. In the case illustrated in the Figure, E is the excited state resulting from process (1), light absorption.

Any molecule in energy states above the ground state is fundamentally unstable. The molecule tends to reduce the instability either by decomposing or by losing the excess energy in one way or another. In this discussion of photosynthesis, we are concerned only with those processes by which an excited molecule returns to the ground state, and not with the decomposition of the pigments. One possible route is Process (2), the dissipation of heat, followed by Process (4), fluorescence from state D, and Process (10), a second dissipative step. Some pigmented substances, like hemoglobin of the blood, are not fluorescent at all. They may lose all of their excitation energy in the form of heat, following the route of Processes (2) and (3). A molecule that loses all of its excitation energy by a combination of fluorescence and heat dissipation has no energy left for photochemical reactions. In photochemistry an alternative route must be used. Process (5) is a step in which the pigment loses a good deal of energy by transferring it (as chemical energy) to some other molecule or molecules. Usually the other molecules must be in contact with the pigment. This type of photochemical event, which leaves the pigment molecule itself chemically unchanged, is known as *photosensitization;* the pigment is the *sensitizer.*

How quickly do these processes of energy loss occur? For a typical highly colored organic molecule, Process (4), fluorescence, requires between a billionth and one hundredmillionth of a second. The dissipative steps (2) and (10) are about a thousand times faster. Whether the fluorescent state, D, loses its energy by dissipation (3), by fluorescence (4), or by photo-sensitization (5), depends on which of these processes is the fastest. If one of the three processes is very much faster than the other two, the fastest will be the only one to occur. If the individual rates are not greatly different from each other, several processes may occur at the same time. The probability that a given process will occur (rather than another) is proportional to the speed of that process.

Phosphorescence

The first hint that there are additional routes of energy loss from the fluorescent state came from the observation of *phosphorescence,* a second kind of luminescence. Phosphorescence, Process (8), differs from fluorescence in two important respects. It is much slower than fluorescence and its spectrum is shifted to longer wavelengths. Phosphorescence requires between a thousandth of a second and several seconds, depending on the particular substance. This is slow enough to be observed easily by eye even after the exciting light is turned off. Television picture tubes are a familiar example of phosphorescence, and some of their after-images are related to the relative slowness of the phosphorescent process. The shift of the luminescent spectrum means that some dissipative process, (6), links the fluorescent state, D, with the phosphorescent state, C. In the case of chlorophyll *a*, the shift is tremendous, about 2000Å, carrying the phosphorescence into the infra-red.

The slowness of phosphorescence gives the phosphorescent state an advantage over the fluorescent state in promoting photo-sensitization. The longer life of the phosphorescent state gives other molecules more time to come close enough to the excited pigment to take away the energy by photo-sensitization. As a matter of fact, most known photo-sensitization reactions occurring in solutions proceed by way of the phosphorescent state, that is, by Process (9) rather than by Process (5).

In the case of pure chlorophyll-*a* extracts not containing components for a photochemical reaction, about 30 per cent of the excited molecules will fluoresce, and about 70 per cent will enter the phosphorescent state. Any change in these percentages occurring when other chemicals are added to the solution must mean that the added substances are removing some energy by a sensitization process of one kind or another. It is thus possible to follow photo-sensitization by noting changes in the yield of fluorescence or phosphorescence, even without measuring the products of the reaction.

Energy Transfer

The processes just discussed all occur within the pigment molecule itself or within a complex of molecules in contact with the pigment. Another kind of process, known as *sensitized fluorescence*, involves the interaction of two molecules that may be separated from each other in a solution by dozens of molecules of the solvent. The German-born physicist James Franck discovered sensitized fluorescence in atoms in the early 1920's. Other investigators observed it in molecules in the years following World War II. In this event, two kinds of pigment are dissolved in the same medium, and the solution is illuminated with light that can be absorbed by only one of the pigments, called the *donor*. The light emitted from the solution, however, corresponds to the fluorescence spectrum of the other molecule, called the *acceptor*. Apparently the energy of excitation of the donor is transferred to the acceptor, and the acceptor

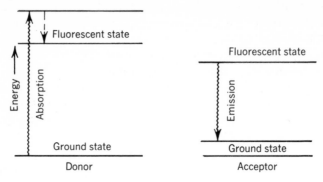

Fig. 7-4. Energy levels of a donor-acceptor system. The donor molecule absorbs light, and the acceptor molecule emits light.

is able to fluoresce as though it had absorbed the light. We say that the donor molecule *sensitizes* the fluorescence of the acceptor by *energy transfer.*

One of the most important principles governing energy transfer is that the fluorescent state of the donor molecule must have an energy greater than or equal to the fluorescent state of the acceptor molecule. This rule is illustrated in Figure 7-4. A typical example is the system of the two chlorophylls, *a* and *b.* The *b* type is found to be a donor for *a,* but *a* is never a donor for *b.* This means that the fluorescent state of *b* has more energy than the fluorescent state of *a.* This result agrees with the fact, mentioned earlier, that the fluorescence of *b* lies at lower wavelengths (with a peak at 6480Å) than that of *a* (with a peak at 6680Å).

Photochemistry

A number of different chemical reactions are photo-sensitized by chlorophyll in solution. Most of the reactions studied are of the oxidation-reduction type. One of the commonest oxidizing agents for these reactions is oxygen gas. The substances whose photo-sensitized oxidations by oxygen gas have been studied include many classes of reducing agents. Another type of sensitized reaction, known as *isomerization,* has recently been discovered. Isomerization is the term for a change in shape of a single molecule, without any change in the number of atoms in the molecule.

Chlorophyll itself undergoes a direct chemical change in some photochemical reactions. The photochemical oxidation and reduction of chlorophyll have both been observed. If the oxidizing or reducing agents are mild, the chlorophyll transformed in the light may return to normal by a reversal of the whole reaction in the dark. When chlorophyll is photo-oxidized by oxygen gas, however, the result is an irreversible destruction of the pigment. Fortunately for the well-being of green plants, the photochemical destruction of chlorophyll by oxygen gas is a relatively slow reaction.

Not all wavelengths of light are equally effective in promoting a photochemical reaction. The differences can be represented in an *action spectrum,* which is a graph showing the relative amount of photochemical activity at each wavelength for equal amounts of incident energy at the various wavelengths. For reactions involving a single pigment, the action spectrum has the same general shape as the absorption spectrum (like those in Figure 7–2). The wavelengths that are most strongly absorbed are the most effective, and those that are only weakly absorbed are the least effective. For most photo-sensitized reactions this relationship can be expressed more precisely in terms of the number of quanta absorbed. All other factors being equal, the amount of photochemical activity is directly proportional to the number of quanta *absorbed* by the pigment at each wavelength. This rule holds for chlorophyll reactions in solution but not, as we shall see in the next chapter, for photosynthesis *in vivo* (that is, in the living organism). Another important difference in chlorophyll's photochemistry *in vivo* as compared to *in vitro* (that is, outside the cell) is that energy is practically never stored by the *in vitro* system. This fact alone sets the photosynthetic process apart from the simpler reactions that can be produced outside the living cell.

8

The Photosynthetic Apparatus

No living cell is simply a random collection of substances. The constituents are arranged according to some structural design, and the functions of the cell depend not only on the components present but also on where they are located. Photosynthesis is no exception. The fixed parts of the cell that contain the materials for absorbing light and for channeling the energy of the excited pigment molecules into a sequence of chemical events is often called the *photosynthetic apparatus.*

The Chloroplast

The green cells of higher plants and green algae cells all contain one or more substructures known as *chloroplasts,* in which the photosynthetic pigments are concentrated. These bodies, the sites of photosynthesis, may be tens of thousands of Angstroms in length and are therefore large enough to be seen under an ordinary light microscope. Figure 8–1 is an electronmicrograph of a *Euglena* cell, showing several chloroplasts. Each chloroplast is bounded by a membrane-like surface. The number of chloroplasts per cell ranges from one to more than a hundred, depending on the particular plant. In many plants the chloroplasts are able to divide and reproduce by themselves. (How they are able to do this is still largely unknown.) It is possible to obtain a preparation of chloroplasts from ground-up cells by centrifugal separations.

A chloroplast may contain up to 10 per cent of its dry weight as pigment, most of which is chlorophyll. Over half of the chloroplast's dry weight is normally protein. Other constituents include lipids (fat-like substances), carbohydrates, nucleic acids, and inorganic minerals.

The electron microscope has shown that the chloroplast itself is highly organized and has a structure of its own. The most striking feature seen in the electronmicrographs of chloroplast preparations is a set of dark discs arranged in almost parallel stacks. Some typical electronmicrographs are shown in Figure 8–2. The chloroplast shown at the top is from a leaf, that on the bottom from a single-celled alga. The disc-like layers, or *lamellae*, appear in both pictures. The leaf sample shows several regions where the layers are stacked very closely together. These dense regions are called *grana*, and the lighter spaces are called the *stroma*, or *matrix*, of the chloroplast.

Properties of the Lamellae

The lamellae are apparently a common structural feature of all photosynthetic organisms, even those that do not contain chloroplasts. Blue-green algae, for example, have no

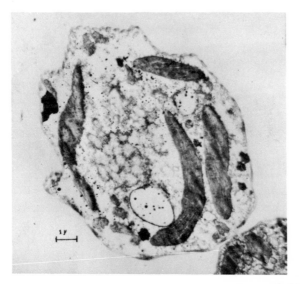

J. J. Wolken

Fig. 8-1. Cross-section of **Euglena,** a single-celled organism. The long, dark, striated structures are chloroplasts. One micron (μ) is one ten-thousandth of a centimeter.

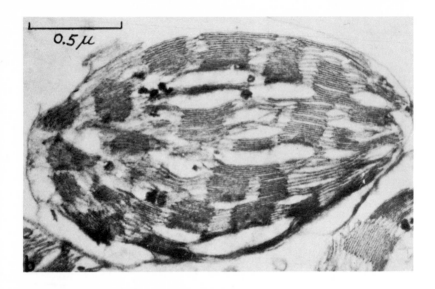

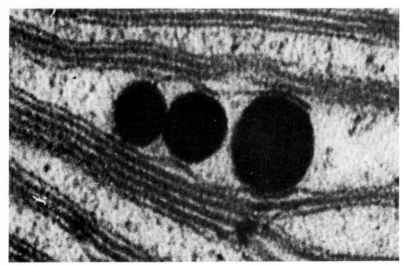

J. J. Wolken

Fig. 8-2. Electronmicrographs of chloroplast cross-sections. Top: Chloroplast of **Elodea canadensis.** The dark regions where the lamellae are tightly stacked are the grana. Bottom: **Euglena** chloroplast; the three dark spots are granules of pigment molecules.

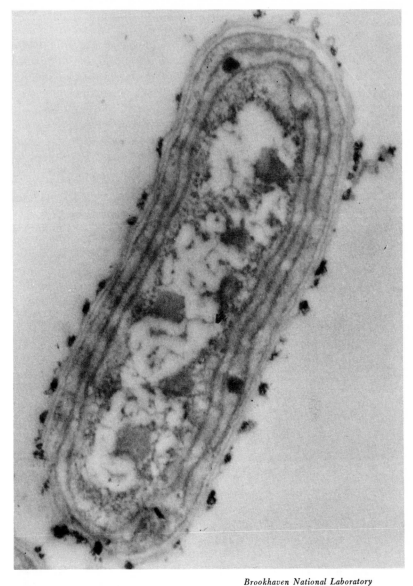

Fig. 8-3. Electronmicrograph of a blue-green alga, **Anacystis nidu-lans.** Lamellae line the inside of the cell membrane.

chloroplasts but do possess pigment-containing lamellae. Figure 8–3 shows a beautiful example of such a case where the lamellae run the whole way around the cell. Photosynthetic bacteria also have layered structures containing the pigments. Some of these bacteria contain small spherical vesicles several hundred to several thousand Angstroms in diameter, called *chromatophores*, in which the pigment is concentrated in a shell-shaped layer. Figure 8–4 is an electronmicrograph of such a bacterial cell. In other bacteria the pigment-bearing lamellae are not differentiated into distinct bodies but are attached to the cytoplasmic membrane that lines the cell wall.

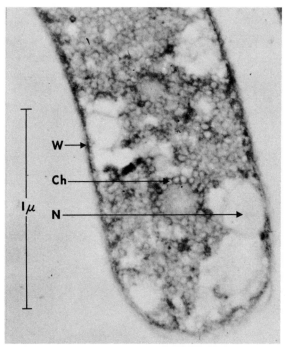

Brookhaven National Laboratory

Fig. 8-4. Electronmicrograph of a purple sulfur bacterium, **Chromatium.** The cell is filled with chromatophores (Ch.), which bear pigment in their outermost shell. Diffuse non-opaque regions (N) and the cell wall (W) also appear.

No electron microscope is powerful enough to show the individual pigment molecules. It has been almost definitely proved, however, that the chlorophyll and carotenoid molecules are concentrated in the lamellae, in practically molecule-to-molecule contact. The lamellar discs themselves have a complex structure and seem to be made up of separate lipid and protein layers, arranged according to a definite pattern resembling that of a club sandwich. The average thickness of the "sandwich" in many photosynthetic organisms is about 200Å. Each sandwich contains several layers of protein and of lipid, and the spaces between the sandwiches are filled with an aqueous solution. The grana of the higher plant chloroplasts are thus stacks of these more fundamental sandwiches. (See Figure 8–7.)

The pigment molecules, highly concentrated in almost two-dimensional layers, have some properties different from those of extracted pigment in solution. The first difference to be recognized appeared in the absorption spectra. For example, the wavelength of maximum red-light absorption by chlorophyll a dissolved in ether is 6620Å. The chlorophyll a in the plant cell has its maximum absorption shifted by as much as several hundred Angstroms to longer wavelengths. (Figure 8–5 shows the absorption spectrum of a *Chlorella* suspension.) The exact location of the absorption peak depends on the state of development of the cell and on the pigment concentration. Careful study has resolved the chlorophyll-a part of the absorption spectrum of the whole cell into two or three separate components. In a typical case, chlorophyll-a peaks were found simultaneously at 6700, 6830, and 6950Å with special methods developed by C. S. French of the Carnegie Institution in Stanford. The component absorbing at 6950Å normally was a small percentage of the total. Spectroscopic examination of chlorophyll extracts has shown that these wavelengths all represent forms of chlorophyll a. Only one long-wavelength peak appears in the extracts, the well-known 6620Å peak of chlorophyll a. The slight shifts in the *in vivo* spectrum must be due to the interactions of chlorophyll a with its neighbors. It is well known that shifts occur when pigment

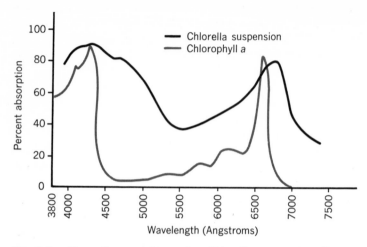

Fig. 8-5. Absorption spectrum of a **Chlorella** suspension. For purposes of reference, the **in vitro** absorption spectrum of chlorophyll **a** (Fig. 7-2) has been included here.

molecules form chemical attachments to other substances. In the case of the photosynthetic pigments, the chlorophyll is certainly bound to the protein layers. Also, since the chlorophyll molecules are in very close contact with each other, a type of crystallization may result that could cause small changes in the absorption spectrum. In a heterogeneous structure like the lamellar discs it is not surprising that there may be two or three kinds of natural chlorophyll-*a* complexes *differing only in the nature of the attachment* of a single type of chlorophyll *a* to its neighbors. On extraction, the "attachments" of the pigment are broken and the resulting dilute solution contains isolated chlorophyll-*a* molecules, each surrounded only by the extracting solvent. The existence of only one chlorophyll-*a* component in the absorption spectrum of the extract is thus explained.

A second difference between *in vivo* and *in vitro* forms of chlorophyll *a* is the extent of its fluorescence. We saw in Chapter 7 that an excited chlorophyll-*a* molecule dissolved in organic solvents has about a 30 per cent probability of emitting fluorescence. This probability is reduced to about 6 per cent for the intact lamellae, even when photosynthesis is prevented by CO_2-starvation. This striking difference shows how strong the influence of the close packing of molecules can be on the processes of energy loss by excited pigment molecules.

The Functional Photosynthetic Unit

There was evidence for the cooperative interaction of many pigment molecules in photosynthesis even before the electron microscope revealed the structural ordering of the lamellae in the early 1950's. The first hint that the chlorophyll molecules do not act independently came from flashing-light experiments performed in 1932. We saw in Chapter 4 that the maximum amount of photosynthesis in a series of flashes can be obtained only if the dark period between flashes is long enough to allow the limiting dark reaction to run its course. Let us now return to the same experiment and ask: What is the *maximum* amount of photosynthetic product *per flash* if the dark time is long enough and all the other conditions are the most favorable? The result depends on the sample, but the *largest yield per flash* reported for *Chlorella* is one molecule of oxygen for 1600 chlorophyll molecules.

The fact that plants have many more chlorophyll molecules than they can use at one time might seem to indicate a waste of chlorophyll. When we recall (Chapter 4) that eight quanta of light must be absorbed in order for one molecule of oxygen to be produced, we see that the apparent discrepancy is greatly reduced. Thus the result of the flash experiment may be stated as follows: the greatest use of light per flash is *eight quanta per 1600 chlorophyll molecules*, or *one quantum per 200 molecules*. Since, according to Einstein's Law of Photochemistry, one molecule of pigment (chlorophyll) can handle only one quantum at a time, we conclude that only one chlorophyll molecule out of every 200 can make use of light energy in a short flash. Does this mean that the other 199 chlorophyll molecules are dead weight, contributing nothing to the photosynthetic process? The answer to this question must be *no* for the following reason. Since all chlorophyll molecules in the chloroplast have the same ability to absorb light (if we disregard the slight shifts in absorption spectrum among the various types of chlorophyll), then 199/200 of all the light absorbed would be wasted were there only one special molecule participating. This prediction would not lead to any difficulties in explaining the results at very high light intensity, where much of the incoming light is wasted anyway, because of the inability of the dark reactions to keep up with the photochemical reactions. It would be very difficult, however, to explain the facts of photosynthesis at low light intensity, where almost every quantum of absorbed light is used for photosynthesis (except for the slight loss of energy through fluorescence) and the percentage energy conversion is very high (region x in Figure 4–1).

A theoretical interpretation of these facts was first proposed in 1936 by Hans Gaffron and K. Wohl, working at that time in Berlin. They reasoned that although all chlorophyll molecules could be used, a limitation on the amount of energy that could be handled at one instant must arise from the short supply of some other essential ingredient (presumably in the ratio of one molecule for every 200 chlorophyll molecules). Gaffron and Wohl constructed a model of 200 chlorophyll molecules, arranged close to each other, in a *photosynthetic unit*. (See Figure 8–6.) The energy of excitation (from light

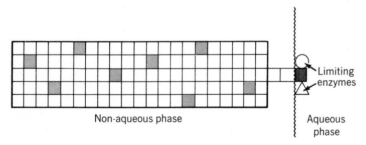

Non-aqueous phase   Aqueous phase

Limiting enzymes

Fig. 8-6. Schematic model of a photosynthetic unit. Open squares represent protected chlorophyll molecules; hatched squares, carotenoids; and cross-hatched squares, exposed chlorophyll **a**.

absorption) of any one chlorophyll molecule within the unit could be transferred to any of its neighbors and, by repeated transfers, even to a distant chlorophyll molecule within the unit. At some point in the unit, a particular chlorophyll molecule was in contact with one or two enzyme molecules. These enzymes were involved in the photochemical reaction itself. A photochemical reaction occurred only when the energy of excitation arrived at this one particular chlorophyll. The reason that only one quantum of energy could be processed (by one unit) in a single flash is that each enzyme could handle only one molecule of the photochemical product at a time. The enzyme required a certain "working period" to do its job and to return for another molecule, and this working period was longer than the duration of the flash.

According to the concept of the photosynthetic unit, most of the pigment molecules serve merely as light absorbers, that is, energy collectors. The large number of these molecules provides a high probability that incident light will be absorbed. Although pigments can take care of the job of light absorption, other substances, including the limiting enzymes, are needed for the actual photochemical reactions. The ability of one set of enzymes to service 200 or so pigment molecules is a wonderful example of the economy of nature.

This model explained a fact that had bothered scientists for a long time. Chlorophyll is fat-soluble, but it does not dissolve in water. For this reason the chlorophyll molecules in the lamellae tend to avoid the water regions of the cell and to accumulate in the lipid layers, probably in close contact with protein layers. The photochemical reactions of photosynthesis, however, ultimately involve water-soluble substances, including CO_2, the carbon intermediates, and phosphoric acid, none of which dissolves readily in lipids. How can chlorophyll, concentrated in a non-aqueous region, be used for the photochemical conversions of substances dissolved in a water phase? James Franck answered this question by pointing out that most of the pigment molecules of the unit are indeed in a lipid, non-aqueous medium, but that the *one* chlorophyll attached to the limiting enzymes is at the end of the unit, at the interface between the non-aqueous and the aqueous regions. He called this one chlorophyll the *exposed* chlorophyll, in contrast to all the other *protected* chlorophylls. Since the exposed chlorophyll is dipping into the water, as it were, any of the water-soluble reactants or intermediates has access to it. The exposed chlorophyll has also been called the *trapping center*, because it traps energy of excitation from any other pigment molecule in the unit. The exposed chlorophyll, together with its attached limiting enzymes, has also been called the *reaction site* of the unit, because it is the point at which the photochemical reactions take place.

We can even make intelligent guesses about what limiting enzymes are attached to the reaction site. One of them may be cytochrome f, which is oxidized as a result of the first photochemical reaction (Chapter 6). (In photosynthetic bacteria, another cytochrome, c, seems to perform the same function.) It is known, in fact, that the cytochrome f in the photosynthetic apparatus is not easily extracted. It appears to be bound tightly to other substances. The total amount of cytochrome f present, as determined by analyses of different plants, corresponds to one molecule for every 200 or 300 chlorophyll molecules, in agreement with the Gaffron-Wohl model. The amount of cytochrome f oxidized in difference-spectroscopy experiments also corresponds to one molecule in about 200 or 300 chlorophyll molecules. The unknown substance Y, which must be oxidized in a second photochemical step, is probably also attached to the exposed chlorophyll, although this conclusion is based largely on indirect evidence. The carbon intermediates are probably not attached to the exposed chlorophyll but are in solution in the surrounding water and participate with the fixed members of the photosynthetic apparatus either directly or indirectly by the normal chemical procedure of random collisions.

The transfer of excitation energy from one pigment molecule to another is an essential requirement of the photosynthetic unit. Is there direct proof that this type of transfer actually occurs? The easiest type of energy transfer to verify experimentally is the type that leads to sensitized fluorescence

(Chapter 7). In the green algae, for example, chlorophyll-*a* fluorescence is observed when light is absorbed not only by chlorophyll *a* itself but by chlorophyll *b* and the carotenoids as well. The reverse processes do not occur; absorption of light by chlorophyll *a* does not lead to fluorescence of chlorophyll *b* or the carotenoids. These experiments prove that chlorophyll *a* can receive energy by transfer from the other pigments. The direction of transfer agrees with the rules governing such processes discussed in Chapter 7. Of all the photosynthetic pigments in green plants, chlorophyll *a* has its fluorescence at the longest-wavelength. In other words, the energy of excitation of the other pigments is always greater than the energy of the fluorescent state of chlorophyll *a*, and the transfer of excitation energy is always from the other pigments to chlorophyll *a*.

Light absorbed by chlorophyll *b* and the carotenoids can be used for photosynthesis, but only indirectly by way of energy transfer to chlorophyll *a*. The evidence for this conclusion comes from experiments showing that the relative efficiency of one of these pigments in sensitizing chlorophyll-*a* fluorescence is exactly the same as its efficiency for photosynthesis. For example, in *Chlorella* a quantum of light absorbed by chlorophyll *b* has the same efficiency as a quantum absorbed by chlorophyll *a* in promoting either chlorophyll-*a* fluorescence or photosynthesis. A quantum absorbed by the carotenoids, on the other hand, is only 40 per cent as efficient as a quantum absorbed by chlorophyll *a* in promoting either chlorophyll-*a* fluorescence or photosynthesis. In other words, transfer of excitation energy from chlorophyll *b* to *a* is 100 per cent efficient, but transfer of excitation from the carotenoids to chlorophyll *a* is only 40 per cent efficient. The probability that a chlorophyll-*a* molecule uses its excitation energy for fluorescence or for photosynthesis is the same, regardless of whether it receives its excitation energy by direct light absorption or by energy transfer from another pigment. Chlorophyll *a* is thus the principal photosentizing pigment in the green plants, and the others are often called *auxiliary pigments*. (Bacteriochlorophyll is the principal photosensitizing pigment in the photosynthetic bacteria.) The exposed chlorophyll of the photosynthetic unit must be a chlorophyll-*a* molecule, because energy must flow to it. The carotenoids and chlorophyll-*b* molecules must be located within the unit.

Energy must flow not only from the auxiliary pigments to the exposed chlorophyll *a*, but also from all the protected chlorophyll *a* molecules of the unit to the exposed one, if the proposed model for the functioning of the unit is correct. This type of energy transfer cannot be proved experimentally by the method of sensitized fluorescence, since there would not be an appreciable change in the fluorescence spectrum if an exposed rather than a protected chlorophyll-*a* molecule fluoresces. There is good reason to think that the same type of transfer of excitation energy occurs between identical molecules. Experiments on the change in fluorescence intensity with changing light intensity have been interpreted as confirmation of such a transfer to the exposed chlorophyll *a*. The transfer is very rapid, as indeed it must be if the excitation is not to be lost by dissipation before it reaches the exposed chlorophyll of the unit. It has been estimated that migration of excitation energy from a protected to an exposed chlorophyll *a* requires only about one hundred-billionth of a second.

The close packing of pigment molecules in the lamellae is necessary for efficient energy transfer. It should be emphasized that the functional photosynthetic unit of 200 or so chlorophyll molecules is a subunit within the much larger structures identified by electron microscopy—the grana, the chromatophores, and even the lamellae themselves. Not much is known about the relative positions of the functional units within the larger structural units; one possible arrangement is shown in the schematic drawing in Figure 8–7.

The Emerson Effect

We concluded in the previous section that chlorophyll *a* is the main green plant photosynthetic pigment for the direct conversion of excitation energy into chemical energy. This statement is not a simple one, since we saw earlier in the chapter that there may be two or three different "forms" of chlorophyll *a* in the plant. On the basis of experiments begun in 1957 by Robert Emerson at the University of Illinois, it has been proposed that these different forms may play different roles in the photosynthetic process.

Fifteen years earlier, Emerson had measured the relative efficiencies of *monochromatic light* (a single wavelength) of different wavelengths for photosynthesis by *Chlorella*. He found, as expected, that the most effective light for photosynthesis was red (6500–6800Å) or blue (4000–5000Å), those colors that are most strongly absorbed by chlorophyll, and that the least effective light was green (5000–6000Å), which is hardly absorbed at all by *Chlorella* (see Figure 8–5). He then tested the law obeyed by photo-sensitized reactions *in vitro* to see whether the amount of photosynthesis was *directly pro-*

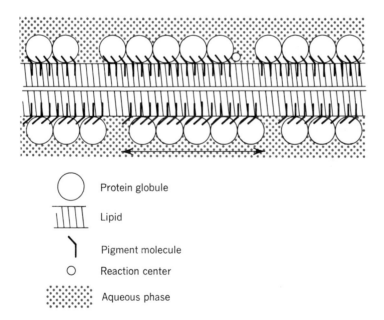

Protein globule

Lipid

Pigment molecule

Reaction center

Aqueous phase

Fig. 8-7. Schematic model of a lamellar cross-section. This model is designed only to show the relative sizes of the different components. The location of the pigment molecule is not known.

portional to the number of quanta *actually absorbed* at each wavelength. He found that this law was not obeyed. Rather, a quantum absorbed at 6800Å was 36 per cent more effective than a quantum absorbed at 4900Å. This finding was easy to explain because light at 6800Å is absorbed only by chlorophyll *a*, which can use the energy *directly* for photosynthesis; light at 4900Å, on the other hand, is absorbed mainly by the carotenoids, which use their energy for photosynthesis only *indirectly*, by an inefficient transfer to chlorophyll *a*. Emerson also observed that the effectiveness *per absorbed quantum* sharply decreased as the wavelength increased, starting at 6850Å. This fact was difficult to explain because chlorophyll *a*, the only known pigment absorbing in this wavelength region, was thought to use its excitation energy directly.

In more recent experiments Emerson found that light above 6850Å (let us call this *far-red* light) is more effective than the previous experiments had led him to believe. Particularly, photosynthesis done in the presence of two beams of light, one in the *far-red* (above 6850Å) and one in the *red* (6500–6850Å), was more than the sum of the amounts of photosynthesis done in separate experiments with the individual beams. In one experiment, the amounts of oxygen produced per minute, in relative units, were 100 in the red beam, 20 for the far-red beam, and 160 for the combined beams. The extra amount, called the *enhancement* (160 − 120 = 40), represents some stimulation of the effect of one beam by the other. Since the red beam alone gave the maximum possible quantum efficiency, the enhancement could not be attributed to an increase in the efficiency of the red light. Thus the enhancement must have been due to an *increased efficiency of far-red light in the presence of red light*. This phenomenon is now known as the *Emerson effect*.

The generally accepted explanation for the Emerson effect is the following. Above 6850Å an appreciable fraction of the absorbed light is absorbed by one of the minor components of chlorophyll *a*, which we shall call "P7000" because it is a *pigment* whose maximum absorption of red light occurs at about 7000Å. (This might be the same minor component discussed earlier in this chapter—the one found by French that absorbs at 6950Å.) Below 6850Å most of the absorption is due to chlorophyll *b* and the major chlorophyll-*a* component. Clearly then, there are two different photochemical steps in photosynthesis. Energy reaching P7000-molecules can be used only for the first of these reactions. Both photochemical reactions are essential steps; without either of them photosynthesis would stop. In far-red light, there is very little photosynthesis because the second photochemical step cannot take place. When red light is added to far-red, the *red* can sensitize the second step and the *far-red* the first step, allowing both light beams to be used efficiently.

Since the absorption maximum of P7000 is at the longer wavelength (lower energy), it would be the pigment toward which excitation energy should normally flow by energy-transfer processes from all other neighboring pigment molecules. Energy cannot flow from P7000 to the normal chlorophyll. Why, then, is there not a flow of all excitation energy to P7000, resulting in inefficient photosynthesis, even when light is absorbed below 6850Å by the normal chlorophyll? The answer must be that P7000 is not distributed uniformly throughout the lamellae but is located only in certain photosynthetic units. Energy transfer occurs only within the unit, and not from one unit to another. Units containing P7000 have been termed *pigment-system-1* units; the others are termed *pigment-system-2 units.* System-1 units can sensitize only the first photochemical step. System-2 units can sensitize the second step and (according to some, but not all, interpretations) the first as well. These relationships are summarized in the diagram of energy flow in green plants on the next page.

Straight arrows in the diagram show the direction of flow of excitation energy within the units. The wavy arrows represent photo-sensitization. In pigment system 1, P7000 serves as a temporary trap for excitation energy resulting from light absorption by any of the pigments in this system. In pigment system 2, the exposed chlorophyll *a* serves as a trap for excitation energy resulting from light absorption by any of the pigments in this system.

Pigment System 1   Pigment System 2

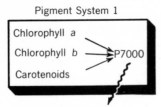   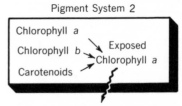

First photochemical step   Second (and first?) photochemical step

The distribution of the pigments is more complicated in the red and blue-green algae. The phycobilin pigments, found only in non-green algae, are probably not localized in the lamellae that contain the chlorophyll. They seem to be concentrated in an aqueous medium that makes contact only with the *exposed* chlorophylls of the units. In spite of the fact that the phycobilins are not imbedded in the chlorophyll units, they are still found to sensitize the fluorescence of chlorophyll *a*. Presumably their role, like that of the auxiliary pigments in the green algae, is to absorb light and funnel excitation energy to chlorophyll *a* for photosynthetic purposes. Strangely enough, light absorbed by the phycobilins is more efficient in promoting chlorophyll-*a* fluorescence and photosynthesis than light absorbed by chlorophyll-*a* itself. In double-beam Emerson-effect experiments, phycobilin absorption is found to enhance the effectiveness of light absorbed by chlorophyll *a*. The explanation of this is that most of the chlorophyll *a* is contained in units that possess at least some P7000, namely, pigment-system-1 units. *Any* light absorbed by these units, whether by the P7000 itself or by the normal chlorophyll, will result in a transfer of excitation energy to P7000, which can lead only to the first photochemical step. On the other hand, if light is absorbed by the phycobilins, the energy is transferred directly to an *exposed* molecule of chlorophyll *a* at the edge of a unit, which can use the energy directly for the photochemical reactions of photosynthesis. The following diagram summarizes the flow of excitation energy in red and blue-green algae.

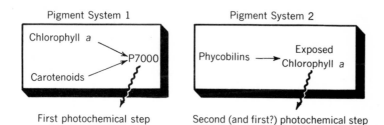

First photochemical step   Second (and first?) photochemical step

The Emerson effect has never been observed in the photosynthetic bacteria. That is, there is no decrease in the effectiveness of absorbed quanta at long wavelengths, nor is there enhancement of the effectiveness of longer wavelength by adding light of shorter wavelength. This may mean that only one kind of photochemical step occurs in the bacteria, not two as in the green plants.

The Nature of the Two Photochemical Steps

The Emerson effect has provided evidence for the existence of two different essential photochemical reactions in green plant photosynthesis. This conclusion was anticipated in Chapter 6 on the basis of completely different experiments by difference spectroscopy. The energy that must be stored in the oxidation-reduction reactions of photosynthesis is considerable, and the overall difference in S.E.P. of 1.25 volts is more than can be overcome efficiently by one quantum. Although one quantum cannot do the whole job, two could, but the laws of photochemistry demand that there must be two different photochemical steps if two quanta are to be used.

The difference-spectroscopy experiment on poisoned algae (described in Chapter 6) led to the identification of cytochrome f as a substance oxidized in the first photochemical step. This conclusion is supported by other experiments on non-poisoned red algae, *Porphyridium*. With these algae it is easy to select a wavelength of illumination that will allow either chlorophyll a or the phycobilins to absorb most of the energy. Cytochrome f is found to pile up in its oxidized form only when chlorophyll a absorbs all the incident light. This is consistent with the previous discussion of the nature of the pigment systems. Most of the chlorophyll a in *Porphyridium* is located in pigment-system-1 units, which can sensitize only the first photochemical step. If this is the step in which cytochrome f is oxidized, and the second photochemical reaction is the one in which cytochrome f is reduced, the reason for the pile-up of oxidized cytochrome is obvious. When the phycobilins absorb light, however, both photochemical reactions occur at the same rate. As soon as a cytochrome f is oxidized by the first step, it is reduced by the second; thus, the oxidized form does not accumulate.

Other experiments by difference spectroscopy have shown that P7000 itself undergoes a chemical change during illumination at wavelengths that favor pigment-system-1 excitation. This change may be a reversible oxidation. Some workers have interpreted this fact as evidence that P7000 not only causes the photochemical reaction of substances attached to it, but also that it undergoes chemical changes in doing so. Other workers believe that the temporary oxidation of P7000 is not an essential part of the photosynthetic sequence, but is a side reaction that occurs in competition with photosynthesis. This is just one example of the many questions about the mechanism of photosynthesis that will have to be answered through further experimentation.

The photochemical steps involved may be different for bacterial photosynthesis. Oxidation of a related iron-containing protein, cytochrome c, appears to parallel the photochemical oxidation of cytochrome f in green plants. There is no evidence of an Emerson effect, and therefore it cannot be determined whether a second kind of photochemical reaction occurs in the bacteria. In comparing photosynthesis in green plants and bacteria, we find some similarities and some differences. The consensus is that the two processes begin in the same way and then diverge. Whether the divergence occurs before or after the occurrence of a second photochemical step has yet to be determined. The two processes are compared in the chart on the next page.

REACTION SCHEMES FOR GREEN PLANTS AND BACTERIA
Steps Common to Both

$$X(ox) + Cyt(re) \rightsquigarrow X(re) + Cyt(ox)$$
$$X(re) + CO_2 \longrightarrow X(ox) + \text{reduced carbon compounds}$$

Steps in Green Plants	Steps in Bacteria
$Cyt(ox) + Y(re) \rightsquigarrow$ $Cyt(re) + Y(ox)$ $Y(ox) + H_2O \longrightarrow$ $Y(re) + O_2$	$Cyt(ox) + Donor(re) \left(\begin{array}{c} \longrightarrow \\ \text{or} \\ \rightsquigarrow \\ ? \end{array} \right) Cyt(re) + Donor(ox)$

Some Typical Bacterial Donor Couples

Reduced Form	Oxidized Form
H_2S	Sulfur (S)
H_2	H_2O
Fatty Acid	Carbohydrate

Cyt stands for cytochrome (either *f* or *c*). *Ox* and *re* stand for oxidized and reduced respectively. Each equation may actually represent a *series* of reactions having the net effect shown in the diagram. The solid arrows ($\longrightarrow$) represent purely dark reactions. A wavy arrow ($\rightsquigarrow$) represents a reaction or series of reactions involving a photochemical step. The equations as written indicate the starting and final materials, but not necessarily the relative numbers of molecules of the various substances. (These are not balanced equations.)

The reduction of carbon compounds occurs in either case by the intervention of reduced X, which must be made photochemically. In green plants, oxygen production requires the oxidation of Y in a second photochemical step. In photosynthetic bacteria, oxygen is not produced, but some other couple undergoes a net oxidation. The reduced form of this couple is often called the *electron donor*, since it loses (or *donates*) electrons to another couple during its oxidation. It is not known whether the oxidation of this couple requires a second photochemical step. The energy requirements of bacterial photosynthesis are much less than in green plants; thus the total difference in S.E.P. is also smaller for the bacteria. It is therefore a possibility that one quantum is sufficient to do the job.

9

Reactions Outside the Living Cell

Constant reference has been made to the complexity of photosynthesis—to the large number of individual reactions that must be synchronized in the plant cell for the proper functioning of the overall process. Is it possible to break down the photosynthetic apparatus into component parts, each of which promotes just one of the individual steps, and then study the component reactions one at a time? This method of analysis has been applied very successfully to the experimental study of other life processes, such as the oxidation of sugars in respiration. In the case of respiration, biochemists discovered in the 1920's that a single cell contains a large number of enzymes, each of which *catalyzes* a specific chemical reaction. (A *catalyst* is a substance that speeds up a chemical reaction without undergoing permanent chemical change itself.) The various enzymes were separated in the last several decades by chemical separation techniques. Then each catalytic reaction was studied in an aqueous solution containing a single enzyme and the specific chemicals of that reaction. After many years of work on these isolated enzyme systems, biochemists began to find out how the individual reactions are "linked together" in the workings of the living cell.

This approach has also been fairly successful in studying the carbon pathway of photosynthesis. Almost all of the reactions discussed in Chapter 5 are known to be catalyzed by specific enzymes, and in many cases the enzymes have actually been isolated from plant chloroplasts. The procedure is not so simple, however, for the *photochemical* reactions of photosynthesis. One of the problems is connected with solubility. Chlorophyll, as we saw earlier, is not soluble in water. Although organic solvents like ether and alcohol dissolve chlorophyll, they are not good solvents for the substances believed to react directly with the chlorophyll in photosynthesis. As a result, solutions of chlorophyll, although they will sensitize many different photochemical reactions, have never been found to sensitize the production of oxygen from water.

Isolation of Chloroplasts

In 1939, Robert Hill of Cambridge University achieved a major breakthrough in this problem. He discovered that chloroplasts removed from a plant cell still preserve many of the important photochemical properties of the intact organism. We now know that it is not even necessary to preserve a whole chloroplast. The grana of the higher plant chloroplasts, or even smaller fragments that preserve the lamellar structure, possess the same photochemical activity discovered by Hill.

Before discussing the nature of this photochemical activity, it will be helpful to consider the methods of obtaining the active chloroplasts and chloroplast fragments. The leaves of higher plants (spinach and Swiss chard, for example) are ground either by hand or in a mechanical blender. The suspension is first filtered to remove large leaf fragments and is then centrifuged at a slow speed so that whole cells or chunks of cell wall settle out. The clear *supernatant* (literally, the portion that "floats on top") is poured off and centrifuged at a much higher speed. This time the chloroplasts and their fragments, being the heaviest particles in suspension, settle out. The supernatant containing the *cytoplasm,* or cell fluid, is discarded. The chloroplasts may be repeatedly washed and centrifuged to obtain a purer sample.

One of the difficulties of working with chloroplasts is that they are not as stable as whole cells. As soon as the cell is broken, inhibitory substances from other parts of the cell apparently invade the chloroplast. Since the whole cell is necessary to keep the photosynthetic apparatus in good repair in a living plant, chloroplasts cannot be kept more than several hours at room temperature. They are therefore usually stored in a refrigerator or even in a deep freeze, and the whole operation of breaking the cells and isolating the chloroplasts is in fact done in a cold room, with the temperature several degrees above freezing.

The Hill Reaction

If some oxidizing agent R, called a *Hill reagent*, is added to a chloroplast suspension and the mixture is then illuminated, oxygen is evolved and the oxidizing agent is reduced. This is the *Hill reaction*, summarized in the unbalanced equation

$$R(\text{oxidized}) + H_2O \longrightarrow R(\text{reduced}) + O_2$$

The Hill reaction has an obvious similarity to photosynthesis, the photochemical evolution of oxygen. The first Hill reagent was an iron salt. Soon after Hill's original discovery, workers all over the world performed experiments with isolated chloroplasts and extended the list of oxidizing agents that could be used. The list grew rapidly and included dozens of both organic and inorganic oxidizing agents. Some oxidizing agents, including CO_2, were unable to produce the Hill reaction. In other words, the washed chloroplasts could not sustain complete photosynthesis.

Further experiments have proved that the Hill reaction follows many of the individual steps of photosynthesis itself. In experiments with flashing light, many of the results were identical for both processes. The average dark time between flashes necessary to give the maximum yield of oxygen per flash was the same in both cases, about 0.02 second (Chapter 4). The maximum amount of oxygen produced per flash was also the same, about one molecule for every 1600 chlorophyll molecules (Chapter 8). These experiments proved that the factor limiting the maximum rate of photosynthesis is the same as for the Hill reaction. This factor must therefore be a substance attached to the lamellar particles, for it was not washed out in the process of isolating the chloroplasts.

The minimum quantum requirement measured in steady weak light is the same for the Hill reaction as for photo-

synthesis, namely, eight quanta per molecule of oxygen produced. The action spectra are also the same for the two processes. The fact that the relative efficiencies of different wavelengths are the same for the two processes must mean that the
same pigment systems are involved. A more detailed confirmation of this conclusion came from the observation of an Emerson effect in the Hill reaction (Chapter 8). In other words,
far-red light above 6850Å is inefficient in promoting the Hill
reaction, but it becomes increasingly efficient during simultaneous irradiation with light of shorter wavelength.

The above experiments indicate that the number of photochemical steps is the same in the two processes, that the same
pigment systems are used, and that the limitations on maximum oxygen-production rates are also the same. Not only does
the Hill reaction follow the identical *photochemical* steps as
photosynthesis, but also many identical *dark reactions* leading
from the photochemical products to oxygen production.
DCMU, the poison used by Duyseus to inhibit one of the dark
reactions in the oxygen-evolving part of photosynthesis, has
also proved to be a poison for the Hill reaction.

Some parts of photosynthesis do not occur in the Hill reaction, including all the reactions of the carbon cycle. Photosynthetic poisons like cyanide, which do not influence the Hill
reaction, must exert their effect on particular enzymes in the
carbon pathway.

We listed the major energy-storing reactions of green-plant
photosynthesis (Chapter 6) as,

$$X(ox) + Cyt(re) \longrightarrow X(re) + Cyt(ox)$$

and

$$Y(re) + Cyt(ox) \longrightarrow Y(ox) + Cyt(re)$$

where *re, ox,* and *Cyt* stand for oxidized, reduced, and cytochrome *f* respectively. In these terms, cytochrome *f* and Y are
used for both the Hill reaction and photosynthesis. If the second of the above reactions occurs in several steps, then the
individual reactions would be the same for both processes.
Further, the reactions between oxidized-Y and water—producing reduced-Y and oxygen—are the same in photosynthesis

and the Hill reaction. It is not certain whether the naturally occurring X reduced in photosynthesis participates in the Hill reaction. If the same X is reduced, then differences between the two processes occur in the subsequent dark reactions of reduced-X.

In the earliest examples of the Hill reaction, the amount of energy stored in the overall process was always much less than in photosynthesis. That is to say, the S.E.P. of the Hill reagent was much greater algebraically than the -0.43-volt value for the CO_2-glucose couple and the S.E.P. difference that had to be overcome between the Hill reagent and oxygen was less than the 1.25-volt difference for photosynthesis. Subsequently experiments have been performed with other Hill reagents in which as much chemical energy was stored as in photosynthesis itself.

The minimum quantum requirement of eight per molecule of oxygen does not depend on the amount of energy stored by the photochemical process. If the nature of the Hill reagent is varied, the amount of stored energy (per oxygen molecule produced) can be reduced to one-tenth that in photosynthesis, while the number of light quanta required remains fixed. This shows that the photochemical steps are the common factor in many Hill reactions and in photosynthesis. Each photochemical step requires one quantum, regardless of what fraction of the energy of that quantum will be stored in the final stable product of the reaction.

Hill discovered that the photochemical activity associated with photosynthesis does not require the whole cell. It had previously been known that individual chlorophyll molecules in true solution cannot perform this same photosynthetic task. There must be, then, some minimum amount of organization of the photosynthetic apparatus needed to sustain this characteristic activity. Attempts have been made to find out what this minimum structural unit is. Is it the functional photosynthetic unit containing about 200 chlorophyll molecules? There are some who think that it is, but the answer is not known with certainty. We know that the smallest cell particle capable of supporting the Hill reaction must retain the lamellar feature. It must contain the pigments, lipids, and proteins needed to maintain the proper composition of the lamallae, including certain enzymes needed to link the photochemical reactions with the evolution of oxygen. In terms of the reaction schemes, at least the cytochrome-*f* and Y enzymes must be part of the minimum particle. They must be bound so tightly to the particle that they are not washed out during the preparation procedure. Bessel Kok of the Research Institute for Advanced Studies in Baltimore recently confirmed part of this theoretical prediction by showing that cytochrome *f* is so tenaciously bound to chloroplast fragments that it still remained after 85 per cent of the chlorophyll had been removed by an organic solvent.

A reaction paralleling the Hill reaction has subsequently been discovered in chromatophores isolated from photosynthetic bacteria. These particles can carry out a number of photochemically induced oxidation-reduction reactions in which both the oxidizing and reducing agent are added. Oxygen evolution is not observed in these preparations. In many of these reconstructed systems, the amount of energy stored is comparable, per quantum, to that stored by photosynthesis in the intact bacterial cell.

Photophosphorylation

Thus far the discussion of the energy-storage aspects of photosynthesis has dealt with those processes in which electrons are transferred from a reducing agent to an oxidizing agent. Chemistry consists of many types of reactions, and considerable amounts of chemical energy can be stored even when oxidation-reduction does not occur. A particular example, already referred to, is the combination of phosphoric acid with a sugar to form what is called a *sugar phosphate ester*. One of the three energy-storing reactions of the carbon cycle (*h* in Chapter 5) is such a process. This reaction was written in the shortened version as

$$\text{Pentose}(5) \longrightarrow \text{RDP}(5)$$

If water and phosphoric acid are included, and the full name

for the carbohydrates given, the same reaction is represented
by the following equation:

Ribulose Phosphate + Phosporic Acid $\longrightarrow$
$\qquad\qquad$ Ribulose Diphosphate (RDP) + H_2O

This example is typical of a whole category of reactions.
Energy is required if phosphoric acid is to be attached chemically to another substance. The "attachment" is often referred
to as the *phosphate bond,* and the amount of energy stored
during the process is called the *phosphate-bond energy.* The
value of the phosphate-bond energy depends on the nature of
the compound to which phosphoric acid becomes attached.
When the amount of energy is particularly large, compared
with other compounds, the attachment is said to be a *high-
energy phosphate bond.*

The high-energy phosphate bond is extremely important in
the energy budget of living cells. The phosphate bond is an
important way of storing chemical energy for general use. An
animal derives all of its energy from the respiratory oxidation of the food it eats. The energy released in respiration is
partially stored in the form of high-energy phosphate bonds.
This reservoir may be drawn on later to supply the energy
for such purposes as muscular activity and energy-requiring
chemical syntheses needed for growth and the maintenance of
cell functions.

One of the most important biological compounds containing high-energy phosphate bonds is *adenosine triphosphate,*
usually abbreviated ATP. Actually ATP has three phosphate
bonds (as indicated by the *tri* in its name), but only one of
these plays a major part in biological energy-exchange reactions. ATP is formed in an energy-storing process by the
attachment of a third phosphoric acid molecule to *adenosine
diphosphate,* ADP, which already contains two attached phosphoric acid groups:

ADP + Phosphoric Acid $\longrightarrow$ ATP + H_2O

The energy stored in the newly formed high-energy phosphate
bond of ATP may be released if the above reaction is reversed

by some control system within the cell:

$$ATP + H_2O \longrightarrow ADP + \text{Phosphoric Acid} + \text{energy}$$

The phosphate-bond energy is small compared to the energy of oxidation-reduction reactions (only eight per cent of the energy that is released when one molecule of oxygen oxidizes organic matter to carbon dioxide and water). Nevertheless, the energy of phosphate bonds is extremely useful in many biological processes.

Knowing the important role played by ATP in respiration, fermentation, muscle contraction, bioluminescence, and other life processes, many biochemists attempted to determine whether the high-energy phosphate bond played a part in photosynthesis. In 1954 two groups of investigators discovered almost simultaneously that broken-cell preparations can make high-energy phosphate bonds in connection with a photochemical reaction: Albert Frenkel, working with bacterial chromatophores at Harvard University and later at the University of Minnesota, and Daniel Arnon's group at the University of California at Berkeley, with spinach chloroplasts. When a washed-chloroplast (or chromatophore) preparation containing ADP, phosphoric acid, a magnesium salt, and a small amount of an additional substance called a *co-factor*, was illuminated, chemical analysis showed that ATP had been formed. This process is now known as *photophosphorylation*.

The ADP and phosphoric acid are the principal reactants in the formation of ATP. Magnesium salts are required catalysts for most of the known biochemical reactions of ATP. The chloroplasts obviously provide the photochemical apparatus that serves to transform light into chemical energy. The co-factor originally used was vitamin K, but dozens of suitable co-factors have been discovered subsequently. The common feature of all these co-factors is their ability to serve as oxidation-reduction couples; that is, they occur in both oxidized and reduced forms. Since neither the magnesium salt nor the co-factor underwent any permanent change during photophosphorylation, they can be classified as catalysts.

More was learned about the role of the co-factor from later

experiments with the Hill reaction. In these studies, a reaction mixture made up of chloroplasts and a Hill reagent (R) was prepared. ADP, phosphoric acid, and a magnesium salt were added, and the mixture was illuminated. Both the Hill reaction and photophosphorylation were found to take place simultaneously:

$$R(\text{oxidized}) + H_2O \longrightarrow R(\text{reduced}) + O_2$$

$$ADP + \text{Phosphoric Acid} \longrightarrow ATP + H_2O$$

The two reactions appeared to be *coupled* because each stimulated the other. The Hill reagent was necessary for phosphorylation when a co-factor was not present; and the rate of oxygen evolution was in many cases greater in the presence of the phosphorylation ingredients.

Whether a catalytic co-factor or a Hill reagent is used, the photophosphorylation process is essentially the same. The formation of a high-energy phosphate bond in these experiments is somehow or other connected with an oxidation-reduction reaction. When a Hill reagent was added, it was reduced and water was oxidized to oxygen. In the experiment with the catalytic co-factor, however, no net oxidation or reduction was observed. This paradox was resolved by assuming that the oxidized form of the co-factor really served as a Hill reagent and was reduced, but that the reduced form was quickly re-oxidized by the oxygen. This is summarized as:

$$\text{Co-factor}(\text{oxidized}) + H_2O \longrightarrow \text{Co-factor}(\text{reduced}) + O_2$$

$$ADP + \text{Phosphoric Acid} \longrightarrow ATP + H_2O$$

$$\text{Co-factor}(\text{reduced}) + O_2 \longrightarrow \text{Co-factor}(\text{oxidized}) + H_2O$$

Net result:

$$ADP + \text{Phosphoric Acid} \longrightarrow ATP + H_2O$$

According to this scheme, the co-factor can be used over and over again and does not suffer any permanent change. For that reason, the process occurring with added co-factor is called *cyclic photophosphorylation*. The process occurring when a net Hill reaction occurs, that is, a measurable production of oxygen and reduction of the Hill reagent, is known as *non-cyclic photophosphorylation*.

Cyclic and non-cyclic photophosphorylation are very similar. Definite proof has been obtained by carrying out cyclic photophosphorylation in an atmosphere of oxygen containing the isotope O^{18}. Although no net consumption or production of oxygen gas occurred during illumination, the oxygen gas was found to change its isotopic composition. This meant that normal O^{16} atoms, initially present in the water, were changing places with the O^{18} atoms of the oxygen gas. These atoms could not have changed places unless there had been some specific chemical mechanism for the exchange. The cyclic reaction scheme satisfactorily accounts for the facts: oxygen atoms from the water become oxygen gas atoms by means of the oxygen-evolution step; oxygen atoms from the gas become oxygen atoms of the water by the step involving the re-oxidation of the co-factor.

There are a few co-factors of cyclic photophosphorylation that do not induce the exchange of oxygen isotopes. For these cases the above scheme must be abandoned. It is still possible to assume that the co-factor is reduced in the light and then re-oxidized in the dark, but that the re-oxidation takes place by way of one of the intermediates leading to oxygen rather than by oxygen gas itself. In Chapter 6 it was pointed out that *at least* two such intermediates must exist, oxidized cytochrome f and the unknown substance Y. Letting 'I' stand for either one or possibly a third intermediate on the way to oxygen production, we can write a schematic set of equations for cyclic photophosphorylation as follows:

Co-factor(oxidized) + I(reduced) $\longrightarrow$
                    Co-factor(reduced) + I(oxidized)

ADP + Phosphoric Acid $\longrightarrow$ ATP + H_2O

Co-factor(reduced) + I(oxidized) $\longrightarrow$
                    Co-factor(oxidized) + I(reduced)

Net result: ADP + Phosphoric Acid $\longrightarrow$ ATP + H_2O

This generalized scheme is more difficult to prove because the isotopic method cannot be used. One experimental proof is the observation that cyclic photophosphorylation with this type of co-factor proceeded efficiently when the reaction mixture was illuminated with *far-red* light at wavelengths above 7000Å. This kind of light is known to bring about the first photochemical reaction producing cytochrome *f* oxidation—but not the second reaction leading to Y oxidation and to oxygen gas. In this case, the I used for re-oxidizing the co-factor must be some intermediate that precedes the second photochemical step.

We expect a coupling of the phosphorylation step with oxidation-reduction for theoretical reasons. Oxidation-reduction reactions often produce a good deal of energy, enough to supply the energy needed for making ATP from ADP and phosphoric acid. The true *photochemical* oxidation-reduction reactions of photosynthesis and of the chloroplast reactions are not of the *energy-producing* type. On the contrary, they require the *input* of light energy to make them go. Just as the true photochemical reactions of photosynthesis do not produce glucose itself, so the true photochemical reactions of the chloroplast do not directly produce the reduced form of the Hill reagent or of the phosphorylation co-factor. In the case of photosynthesis we used the symbol X for the couple that is primarily reduced in the light and that has a lower S.E.P. than the carbon intermediates reduced in the dark. The greater the difference of S.E.P. between X and the carbon-compound couple, the more energy is available when the direct photoproduct reduces the carbon compounds. In other words:

$$X(\text{reduced}) + CO_2 \longrightarrow$$
$$X(\text{oxidized}) + \text{reduced carbon compounds}$$

Given a sufficient excess of energy, photophosphorylation might be coupled to this *dark* step. Other points in the oxidation-reduction scheme of Figure 6–2 have been suggested as points of coupling with photophosphorylation.

There is experimental proof that the actual phosphorylation does not occur directly in a photochemical step. A. T. Jagendorf, of Johns Hopkins University, illuminated chloroplasts in the presence of a co-factor, but did not add the ADP, phosphoric acid, and magnesium salt until the light was turned off. He found that ATP was quickly formed in the dark. Just as the synthesis of carbohydrates in photosynthesis is not a photochemical reaction, so the so-called photophosphorylation is also a non-photochemical reaction. More chemical energy is stored in the light reactions than is needed to make the final products of the main oxidation-reduction sequence. The immediate light products then undergo a set of dark reactions in which they can afford to waste some of the excess energy. If the amount of energy released in one of these dark reactions is large enough, it might be partly captured and stored in the form of a high-energy phosphate bond.

Photophosphorylation has been observed in isolated chloroplasts. Does it also occur in the whole cell as part of photosynthesis? The same procedures used for studying the chloroplast reactions cannot be used with whole cells because phosphoric acid, ADP, and most co-factors do not easily penetrate the cell membrane. Although there is no clear-cut experimental proof, most investigators agree that some phosphorylation does occur in photosynthesis, because ADP, phosphoric acid, and magnesium salts are found in the cell. They also expect it to occur because the energy for the carbon cycle of photosynthesis could be partially supplied by high-energy phosphate bonds in at least one place. In the reaction

Ribulose Phosphate + Phosphoric Acid $\longrightarrow$
Ribulose Diphosphate + H_2O

the energy needed to form ribulose diphosphate could be supplied by ATP. The ATP production could be coupled with one of the other steps so that the phosphorylation would not require additional quanta above the number necessary for the oxidation-reduction part of photosynthesis. The formation of ATP or some other high-energy phosphate compound may very well be a major chemical part of photosynthesis. It is not yet known which oxidation-reduction reaction or reactions are coupled to phosphorylation.

Photosynthesis *in vitro*

As we have seen, isolated chloroplasts are capable of carrying out a number of photochemical reactions, including the Hill reaction, in all its variations, and photophosphorylation. Can conditions be found under which chloroplasts will carry out full photosynthesis? This indeed has been done by preparing a mixture containing the ingredients for a Hill reaction, for photophosphorylation, and for all the dark enzymatic reactions of the carbon cycle. The Hill reagent must have a low S.E.P. compared with the S.E.P. of the CO_2-glucose couple. The ingredients for photophosphorylation are ADP, phosphoric acid, and magnesium salts; and for the carbon cycle, they are CO_2, enzymes, and at least one of the carbon intermediates. The enzymes are most easily obtained from the supernatant aqueous solution that is normally thrown away after chloroplasts are centrifuged out. A carbon intermediate is added as a pump primer. The reconstituted system will eventually make its own RDP if it achieves photosynthesis, but it needs a small amount of RDP, glucose, or some other carbon intermediate to get things started.

Such synthetic systems have been successfully used to produce oxygen in the light and form sugars by the natural carbon pathway. *Ferredoxin,* one Hill reagent that works in these systems, is worth noting. It is an iron-containing protein found in chloroplasts, but is normally washed out during chloroplast isolation. The S.E.P. for the ferredoxin couple is -0.43 volt, low enough to enable it to reduce carbon compounds. Ferredoxin is also known to react readily with NADP, another naturally occurring couple found in chloroplasts. The following set of reactions (unbalanced and in abbreviated form) has been carried out photochemically in a reconstituted chloroplast system:

$$\text{Ferredoxin(oxidized)} + H_2O \rightsquigarrow$$
$$\text{Ferredoxin(reduced)} + O_2$$

$$\text{Ferredoxin(reduced)} + \text{NADP(oxidized)} \longrightarrow$$
$$\text{Ferredoxin (oxidized)} + \text{NADP (reduced)}$$

$$CO_2 + RDP \longrightarrow 2\ PGA$$

$$ADP + \text{Phosphoric Acid} \rightsquigarrow$$
$$ATP + H_2O$$

$$NADP(\text{reduced}) + ATP + PGA \longrightarrow$$
$$\text{Triose} + \text{Phosphoric Acid} + ADP$$
$$+ H_2O + NADP(\text{oxidized})$$

$$\text{Triose} \xrightarrow[\quad]{\text{(by way of the full carbon cycle)}}$$
$$RDP + \{CH_2O\}$$

Net result: $$CO_2 + H_2O \rightsquigarrow O_2 + \{CH_2O\}$$

The net result of the reconstituted system is the same as that of natural photosynthesis. It is not certain that the ferredoxin-NADP pathway is the only one for reducing carbon compounds, or that it is the natural path used by the intact plant cell. If ferredoxin indeed plays such a role in natural photosynthesis, it may or may not be the *first* substance reduced photochemically, the substance called "X." Continued research is needed to establish the sequence of oxidation-reduction reactions of the *in vivo* system.

The progress already made in understanding physiological oxidation-reduction couples having S.E.P. values close to those required of X far exceeds the progress toward identifying Y. There has been speculation, of course, but no positive identification has yet been made of a physiological couple whose S.E.P. value exceeds 0.80 volt, which Y's must.

Other oxidation-reduction couples are found in chloroplasts, including cytochrome b, a copper-containing protein called *plastocyanin,* and a number of compounds belonging to the classes of *quinones* and *flavins.* Some of these are known to undergo photochemical oxidation or reduction when added to chloroplasts, but their particular roles in natural photosynthesis have not yet been completely sorted out.

10

Conclusion

Survey

Biologists have come a long way in the last 200 years in understanding the elegant machinery by which plants convert light into chemical energy. The first observations were that light, CO_2, and water were the principal raw materials of photosynthesis in green plants, and oxygen and organic compounds the principal products. More refined methods of science have revealed many more details of this complicated process.

The light-absorbing pigments are arranged in the chloroplasts and chromatophores in a manner particularly suited for the collection of energy and for its transfer to special locations where the reactants can make use of it with the help of plant enzymes. The primary photochemical steps are oxidation-reduction reactions whose principal products are a powerful reducing agent and a powerful oxidizing agent. These products then set off a whole chain of dark reactions. The primary reducing agent, X, is used for the reduction of carbon compounds; the primary oxidizing agent is used for the production of oxygen gas in the case of the green plants (this is the substance Y), and for the oxidation of some electron donor in the case of the photosynthetic bacteria.

The dark reactions serve several different purposes: to form energy-rich carbohydrates for future use by the plant; to make some intermediate carbon compounds needed for the absorption of CO_2; to build up short-term stores of energy in the form of high-energy phosphate compounds; and to make the hundreds of different fats, proteins, carbohydrates, and other organic compounds needed for life and growth.

As we have seen, many different approaches are needed to study this complex biological process. We have applied the method of analysis to understand the individual parts of which the whole is constituted. We have seen that each of the individual steps obeys the laws of chemistry and physics, and we have come to see the need for considering all the basic sciences as a unified body of knowledge and procedure.

Remaining Problems

Needless to say, this book has left out much that is known about photosynthesis, but there is much more that needs to be explained. At the very least biochemists would like to know the detailed chemical equations of each successive step of photosynthesis. But there are other important questions to be answered as well.

Why is chlorophyll the only pigment that can perform the actual photochemical steps of photosynthesis? In the broad field of *in vitro* photochemistry, hundreds of dyes are known that can carry out photo-sensitizations, but in plants chlorophyll is truly nature's wonder ingredient. Only chlorophyll *a*, of all the photosynthetic pigments, actually engages in the photochemical reactions of photosynthesis in green plants. In the bacteria, bacteriochlorophyll plays this role. Is there some particular grouping of atoms in chlorophyll that makes it suitable for this significant role? Is the shape of the whole molecule, the distribution of electrons in the excited state, or some other property responsible for making this such a unique substance? The answers to these questions will also answer the basic question of what chlorophyll does when it sensitizes the oxidation-reduction reactions of photosynthesis.

How are the two different kinds of photochemical reaction occurring in green-plant photosynthesis coupled to each other? Why can pigment system 1 perform only one of these two reactions? Is it because the exposed chlorophyll of pigment system 1 is attached to a deficient enzyme system, or because it receives, from the protected pigment molecules of its unit, less than the normal amount of excitation energy?

How is chlorophyll in the plant protected against photo-oxidative destruction? Chlorophyll dissolved in an organic solvent is quickly destroyed when illuminated in the air. Does the lamellar structure have something to do with protecting chlorophyll against oxygen *in vivo?* Do the carotenoids help protect chlorophyll by reacting preferentially with oxygen? Is chlorophyll in fact oxidized *in vivo,* but quickly restored by some built-in recovery process?

At what particular point in the mechanism do variant reactions occur that are not part of photosynthesis proper? It is well known that although enzymes are normally very specific in the chemicals they will catalyze, photo-sensitizing pigments as a rule are not. In the Hill reaction and in cyclic photophosphorylation reactions with added co-factors, a whole category of similar reactions have been observed. At which point in the reaction scheme is there a branching that leads to hundreds of different end products? How do photosynthetic bacteria adapt to such a large variety of electron donors?

What is the simplest type of photosynthetic apparatus that exists in nature? How did the first photosynthetic organisms evolve, and what are the evolutionary relationships among the various kinds of photosynthesizing cells? What can we learn from the evolutionary development of photosynthesis to help us understand the chemical and geological environments that were favorable to the development of the first forms of life?

How does a living cell make use of its primary photosynthetic products for the synthesis of the hundreds of organic compounds that it must make? What are the control mechanisms that "switch on" one needed synthetic path and "switch off" others? What are the feed-back mechanisms that reduce the rate of photosynthesis when the plant is "overstuffed" and cannot assimilate any more organic products?

Perhaps additional questions will occur to the reader. On statistical grounds there is a high probability that the answer to your question is not known by anyone today. The rate of scientific advance is greater now than in any previous period of history, and we can only hope that answers will be found faster than new questions can be asked.

Goals for Future Study

Some practical applications for the study of photosynthesis have been suggested.

Photosynthesis is the only primary food-producing process on this planet. Food supply and distribution are major problems that have not been solved adequately for even half of the world's population. With increasing progress in sanitation, control of disease, and other public health measures, the world's population is increasing more rapidly today than at any period in the past. The problems of feeding the billions or even tens of billions of human beings will become more acute with each successive generation. The English economist Thomas Malthus predicted over 150 years ago that food would be the ultimate limiting factor in determining the maximum population of the world. Although Malthus was unduly pessimistic in his estimate of how soon this limit would be reached and what the limiting population would be, his basic conclusion is certainly valid, that the earth cannot support more people than it can feed. A deeper understanding of the photosynthetic process may help us to make more efficient use of our natural supply of sunlight and carbon dioxide for increasing the world's food production. The experience of culturing green algae in photosynthetic laboratories has been applied on a pilot-plant scale in the production of huge quantities of algae as protein supplements to human diets. The knowledge gained from flashing-light experiments has also been applied to these studies. For example, stirring a thick algae suspension subjects any given algal cell to alternating periods of light and dark. Such a suspension shows more rapid growth than an equally thick undisturbed suspension.

Photosynthesis has been suggested as a solution to some of the problems connected with space travel. A culture of photosynthesizing cells can, in principle, provide the oxygen needed by astronauts and at the same time remove the CO_2 exhaled into the atmosphere of a space capsule. For longer range objectives of supplying a human colony on the moon, on a planet, or on a permanent space-station, photosynthesis might also be called on to provide the food as well. Although there are other possible solutions to these problems, considerable effort has already gone into tests of the suitability of photosynthetic systems for these special purposes.

Questions of the possibilities of life on other planets imply questions about the existence of energy-storing processes. Although we cannot assume that the photosynthetic systems developed on earth are the only possible methods for harnessing radiant energy in a manner useful for living forms, an understanding of the general features of photosynthesis is certainly a starting point for testing the feasibility of life outside our planet. As more and more information becomes available about the atmosphere, surface temperature, humidity, soil composition, and geographical features of other planets, scientists with the broadest knowledge of the variability of the different types of photosynthesis will be able to make more intelligent guesses about the prospects of life.

But the primary goal for most investigators of photosynthesis is none of the above. Rather it is the goal of understanding one of the most important life processes in the world in which we live. The compulsion to understand as much of our natural world as possible, simply because it is here and we are living in it, is the prime motive for all scientists. Even in a complex problem like photosynthesis, where most of the puzzle pieces are still missing, mapping together a small section of the picture is a satisfying experience for the scientific investigator.

Bibliography

A. Articles written primarily for the non-specialist

1. Historical material
   Gabriel, M. L., and S. Fogel, eds. *Great Experiments in Biology*. Englewood Cliffs, N. J.: Prentice-Hall, 1955. Much of the early history of our understanding of photosynthesis is given by way of reprints of original reports of some of the greatest discoveries.

2. Contemporary articles on the pathway of carbon in photosynthesis
   Bassham, J. A. "New Aspects of Photosynthesis." *Journal of Chemical Education*, Vol. 38, pp. 151–155 (1961).

   Bassham, J. A. "The Path of Carbon in Photosynthesis." *Scientific American*, Vol. 206, No. 6, pp. 88–100 (1962).

   Calvin, M. "The Photosynthesis Story: A Case History." *Journal of Chemical Education*, Vol. 35, pp. 428–432 (1958).

   Calvin, M. "The Path of Carbon in Photosynthesis." *Chemical and Engineering News*, Vol. 31, No. 16, pp. 1622–1625 (1953).

3. Contemporary articles on other aspects of photosynthesis
   Arnon, D. I. "The Role of Light in Photosynthesis." *Scientific American*, Vol. 203, No. 5, pp. 105–118 (1960). A summary of experiments with chloroplasts with emphasis on photophosphorylation and the photochemical reduction of NADP.

   Kamen, M. D. "A Universal Molecule of Living Matter." *Scientific American*, Vol. 199, No. 2, pp. 77–83 (1958). A review of the chemical and evolutionary relationships between chlorophyll and the heme enzymes.

Park, R. B. "Advances in Photosynthesis." *Journal of Chemical Education*, Vol. 39, pp. 424–429 (1962).
A view of the structure of the photosynthetic apparatus and the possible relationships between structure and function.

Rabinowitch, E. I. "Photosynthesis." *Scientific American*, Vol. 179, No. 2, pp. 25–35 (1948).
An account of classical methods for study photosynthesis, from the bare visual observations of several hundred years ago to precise physiological measurements of photosynthetic rates.

Rabinowitch, E. I. "Progress is Photosynthesis." *Scientific American*, Vol. 189, No. 5, pp. 80–84 (1953).
The earliest studies on the structure of the photosynthetic apparatus are reviewed, and some *in vitro* photochemical reactions of chlorophyll are described.

Wald, G. "Life and Light." *Scientific American*, Vol. 201, No. 4, pp. 92–108 (1959).
Photosynthesis is discussed in relationship to other important photobiological processes, including vision.

B. The books in this group were written for students or research scientists specializing in photosynthesis. The language is much more technical than in the preceding group of references, but the willing reader will be able to find in each some sections of a descriptive nature that he will be able to understand.

Bassham, J. A., and M. Calvin. *The Path of Carbon in Photosynthesis*. Englewood Cliffs, N. J.: Prentice-Hall, 1957.

Calvin, M., and Bassham, J. A. *The Photosynthesis of Carbon Compounds*. New York: W. A. Benjamin, Inc., 1962.

Gaffron, H. Chapter 4 in *Plant Physiology*, Vol. IB, pp. 3–277, F. C. Steward, Ed., New York: Academic Press, 1960.

Kamen, Martin D. *Primary Processes in Photosynthesis*. New York: Academic Press, 1963.

Rabinowitch, E. I. *Photosynthesis*. New York: John Wiley (Interscience), Vol. I, 1945; Vol. II, Part 1, 1951; Vol. II, Part 2, 1956.

Glossary

Acceptor. A substance that receives energy from another (donor) substance in a transfer not involving a chemical change.

Actinic light. Light producing an appreciable photochemical effect (compare with *measuring light*).

Action spectrum. A curve that shows the relative efficiency of light at each wavelength in bringing about some chemical or biological change.

Adsorbent. A solid material that can extract a variety of gases or dissolved substances from solution and attach them to its surface.

Algae (singular, **alga**). Lower plants, usually lacking tissue differentiation, capable of oxygen-evolving photosynthesis.

Angstrom unit (Å). A unit of length equal to one hundred-millionth of a centimeter.

ATP. Abbreviation for *adenosine triphosphate*, a naturally occurring chemical participating in the storage and the use of phosphate-bond energy.

Auxiliary (or accessory) pigments. Plant pigments other than chlorophyll that absorb an appreciable part of the light energy used for photosynthesis.

Biliprotein. A protein attached to a pigment chemically related to the bile pigments, such as the phycobilins.

Calorie (or **kilocalorie** or **food calorie**). A unit of energy equal, for practical purposes, to the amount of energy needed to heat 10 grams of water from $0°$ to $100°C$; 1 Calorie = 1 kilocalorie = 1000 calories.

Carotenoids. A group of chemically related yellow, orange, or red fat-soluble pigments containing carbon, hydrogen, and sometimes oxygen atoms.

Catalyst. A substance that promotes an increased rate of chemical reaction without itself undergoing any permanent chemical change.

Chloroplast. A subcellular structure of plants, having a membrane and containing photosynthetic pigments.

Chromatography. The separation of chemical substances based on their relative strengths of adsorption from solution.

117

Chromatophore. A subcellular particle containing photosynthetic pigments; especially abundant in photosynthetic organisms not containing chloroplasts.

Co-factor. A catalyst that, in photophosphorylation, undergoes reversible oxidation and reduction.

Couple. A pair of substances one of which can be produced from the other by oxidation.

Cyclic photophosphorylation. A photophosphorylation not accompanied by oxygen evolution nor by the accumulation of any other product of oxidation or reduction.

Cytochrome. One of a class of heme proteins, serving as enzymes by undergoing reversible oxidation and reduction.

Cytoplasm. The fluid portion of a cell outside the membrane-bounded subcellular structures; in plants, the material not included in the nucleus or the chloroplasts.

Dark reaction. A non-photochemical reaction; that is, a reaction that proceeds independently of the amount of light present.

Difference spectrum. The difference in an absorption spectrum of a sample under two different conditions, as, for example, in light and in dark.

Donor. A substance that transfers energy to another (acceptor) substance in a process not involving any chemical change.

Electron donor. A reducing agent; the substance undergoing net oxidation in bacterial photosynthesis.

Emerson effect. The decrease in photosynthetic yield per quantum at long wavelengths, and the enhancement of this yield when short-wavelength light is used simultaneously.

Empirical formula. A chemical formula showing the relative numbers of atoms of the various elements contained in a substance, not necessarily the actual numbers of these atoms per molecule of the substance.

Energy transfer. The transfer of energy from a donor to an acceptor substance without any chemical change in either.

Enhancement. The increased yield of photosynthesis during simultaneous illumination from two light sources of different wavelengths as compared with the sum of the yields measured separately.

Enzyme. A naturally occurring protein catalyst.

Excitation. The acquisition by a chemical system of more energy than it normally contains, for example by absorption of light.

Excited state. The state of a substance when it possesses more than the minimum amount of energy that it can possess.

Exposed chlorophyll. The one chlorophyll molecule in a unit of several hundred molecules that engages in the direct photochemical reactions of photosynthesis.

Ferredoxin. A naturally occurring, iron-containing, non-heme catalyst that functions in oxidation-reduction reactions.

Far-red light. In the Emerson effect in green plants, light at a wavelength where the photosynthetic efficiency is low but is increased in the presence of light of shorter wavelength.

Fluorescence. The light emitted by a substance immediately after it has absorbed light (in plant pigments within several billionths of a second).

Grana (singular, **granum**). Densely stacked pigment-bearing lamellae in plants.

Ground state (or **unexcited state**). The state of a substance possessing the minimum amount of energy that it can possess.

Heme. One of a particular chemical class of iron-containing pigments; usually found in nature in combination with proteins.

High-energy phosphate bond. A phosphate bond, the breaking of which is associated with the release of appreciably more energy than the breaking of an "average" phosphate bond.

Hill reaction. The photochemical reaction of chloroplasts or chloroplast fragments in which oxygen is produced and some added oxidizing agent is reduced.

Hill reagent. An oxidizing agent that is photochemically reduced in the Hill reaction.

Induction period. The period of time following a change in light intensity during which the rate of photosynthesis approaches a steady value.

In vitro (literally, *in glass*). Occurring outside a living system.

In vivo. Occurring within a living system.

Isotopes. Two forms of an element whose atoms differ in mass.

Lamella (plural, **lamellae**). A layer-like structure; in photosynthetic tissue, the layered structure in which chlorophyll is concentrated.

Light-limiting region. The set of conditions under which the rate of photosynthesis is limited by the intensity of the incident light.

Mass number. The integer closest to the relative mass of an atom on the atomic-weight scale; the sum of the number of protons and neutrons contained in an atomic nucleus.

Mass spectrometer. An instrument for separating atoms and molecules according to their mass and for measuring their mass and quantity.

Measuring light. A weak light for analysis, not strong enough to produce an appreciable photochemical effect (compare actinic light).

Micron (μ). A unit of length equal to one ten-thousandth of a centimeter.

Monochromatic. Referring to light of a single wavelength.

NADP. Abbreviation for *nicotinamide adenine dinucleotide phosphate*, a particular biological substance participating in oxidation-reduction reactions; formerly called TPN.

Non-cyclic photophosphorylation. A photophosphorylation accompanied by the accumulation of products of an oxidation-reduction reaction.

Oxidation. The removal of one or more electrons from a substance.

Oxidized state. The member of a couple with the smaller number of electrons per atom.

Oxidizing agent. A substance which gains electrons from another, so that the latter may become oxidized.

Paper chromatography. Chromatography in which filter paper serves as the adsorbent.

PGA. Abbreviation for *phosphoglyceric acid*, the first stable product of the photosynthetic assimilation of carbon dioxide.

Phosphate bond. The chemical linkage holding together two parts of certain molecules that dissociate, on rupture of this linkage, into phosphoric acid and some other substance.

Phosphate-bond energy. The energy released when phosphoric acid is produced by the rupture of a phosphate bond.

Phosphorescence. A delayed emission (much slower than fluorescence) of light by a substance, following light absorption.

Photophosphorylation. The formation of a high-energy phosphate bond, such as in ATP, as a direct or indirect consequence of light absorption, in preparations of photosynthetic tissues.

Photoreduction. A light-driven process occurring in certain algae following anaerobic incubation, in which hydrogen gas and carbon dioxide react to form water and organic matter.

Photo-sensitization. A photochemical reaction in which the substance that absorbs light does not itself undergo permanent chemical change.

Photosynthetic apparatus. The non-soluble structure of a photosynthetic organism; contains photosynthetic pigments and fixed enzymes for photosynthesis.

Phycobilin. A water-soluble auxiliary pigment with a strong attachment between its protein and pigmented parts, found especially in red and blue-green algae.

Phycocyanin. A blue phycobilin pigment found especially in red and blue-green algae.

Phycoerythrin. A red phycobilin pigment found especially in red algae.

Pigment system 1. In Duysens' notation, that group of pigments capable of promoting efficiently part of the photochemistry of photosynthesis but not the part leading to oxygen evolution.

Pigment system 2. In Duysens' notation, that group of pigments capable of promoting efficiently the photochemical reaction leading to oxygen evolution.

Polarographic method. An analytical method for measuring the amount of oxygen produced in photosynthesis; based on the dependence of the current passed by a platinum cathode on the amount of oxygen in the neighboring fluid.

Quantum (plural, **quanta**). The smallest unit of light energy, the value of which depends on the wavelength; also the unit amount of energy that may be added to or taken from an atom or molecule in a single event.

Quantum requirement of photosynthesis. The number of quanta of light energy that must be absorbed for the photosynthetic production of one molecule of oxygen (or for the fixation of one molecule of carbon dioxide).

RDP. Abbreviation for *ribulose diphosphate,* the photosynthetic intermediate that reacts directly with carbon dioxide.

Red light. In the Emerson effect in green plants, red light at a wavelength short enough for the maximum photosynthetic efficiency to be observed (compare *far-red light*).

Reduced state. The member of a couple with the larger number of electrons per atom.

Reducing agent. A substance that transfers electrons to another, so that the latter is reduced.

Reduction. The addition of one or more electrons to a substance.

Saturation. The maximum rate of photosynthesis for a given temperature and carbon-dioxide concentration, independent of any further increase in light intensity.

Saturation curve. A plot of the rate of photosynthesis versus light intensity, at a fixed temperature and carbon-dioxide concentration.

Sensitized fluorescence. The fluorescence emission by one substance as a consequence of energy transfer from a second substance after the latter has absorbed light.

Sensitizer. A substance that absorbs light and transfers its energy of excitation to a second substance without undergoing any chemical change itself.

Splitting of water. A schematic way of describing photosynthesis as the energy-requiring dissociation of water into a hydrogen-rich reducing fragment and an oxygen-rich oxidizing fragment.

Standard electrode potential (S.E.P.). The relative measure, in volts, of the tendency of a couple to be reduced at a given temperature and acidity, when the concentrations of both oxidized and reduced forms of the couple are at defined standard values.

Stroma. The non-lamellar parts of a chloroplast.

TPN. Abbreviation for *triphosphopyridine nucleotide;* now called NADP.

Tracer. As isotopic form of an element different from the common isotopic form, used to follow the course of some substance containing that element in physical, chemical, or biological processes.

Trapping center. A special place within an array of many pigment molecules that can accept, or trap, excitation energy migrating from any molecule in the array.

X. A symbol for the substance photochemically reduced, the reduced form of which is the strongest reducing agent among all photosynthetic intermediates.

Y. A symbol for the substance photochemically oxidized in photosynthesis, the oxidized form of which can react spontaneously in the dark to produce oxygen.

Index

Holt Library of Science